SUNSHINE OVER CLOVER

GARDENS OF WELLBEING

SUNSHINE OVER CLOVER
GARDENS OF WELLBEING

Sarah Wint

First published in Great Britain in 2016 by Sarah Wint

A Cataloguing in Publication record for
this book is available from the British Library

Designed and printed by
Orphans Press, Leominster, HR6 0LD

ISBN: 978-1-5262-0514-8

For Loulou

Introduction

This tale starts and ends with perhaps the saddest loss of all – that of a child. The loss of our daughter Evie before her birth set me on this path which has, ironically, brought me so much happiness. I end the journey talking to Gay Acres, at Bronant in Wales, about the loss of her 9 year old daughter Lauren. Two bereaved mothers who are among the smiliest people you may ever meet. How do we do it?

I firmly believe it is not just the gentle peaceful solace that nature provides but the irrepressible joy that comes from interacting with our natural world. For Gay and me the sight of a new shoot of green life in spring lifts us higher than we would have imagined possible in the first dark months of our grief.

This zest for life reveals itself in my own garden, where too many gorgeous plants are inexpertly stuffed together in a chaotic riot of lush beauty. In Gay's, it reveals itself in numerous quirky features designed to delight visiting children as well as her own. The day I visit her she says her grandchildren are planning a Mad Hatters Tea Party in the garden and as I walk around Bwlch y Geufford Gardens with Gay and our husbands, we find seemingly hundreds of different spots where young minds can bring any fantasy to life.

"Our England is a garden, and such gardens are not made By singing 'Oh, how beautiful!' and sitting in the shade" wrote Rudyard Kipling, and for me, it is precisely the work – as gentle or hard as you choose to make it – that brings the happiness: The process of hope, nurture and connection brings joy and is very much more important than the result.

Of course results are good too – you only have to turn on the telly to see Alan Titchmarsh or Nick Knowles answering DIY and garden SOS calls, bringing joyful tears to the eyes of normal everyday folk, to see that a beautiful space can be hugely emotionally rewarding. Since the beginning of human existence we have found sustenance, comfort and peace in nature. These days much of our modern lifestyle separates humans from the stuff that makes our planet – indeed we tend to think of nature as separate from us, something we visit or look at from time to time, whereas, of course really we are just another part of it. When we are able to fully relax into it, it's like we've come home, it feels right and our bodies respond to the natural rhythm of life and begin to recalibrate and heal. The disconnect we experience in our offices and cities is thought to be a major contributor to physiological dysfunction and unwellness. As a psychological stress reliever there is little better than nature, for nature expects nothing from us – expects us to be nothing but ourselves.

I spent most of my forties dealing with grief and the accompanying search for meaning in my life – indeed all life – as well as overwhelming feelings of regret and hopelessness. But after the first raw years, my wild untameable garden truly became the mainstay of my life and helped me come to terms with the inexorable cycle of life and death. Eventually I started noticing that other people were being affected by their gardens too – or by their own version of connecting with the natural world. As scientific evidence that 'gardening is good for you' mounted, I thought there were probably many ordinary folk who can testify to this blindingly obvious fact through their own stories. Those stories might make an interesting book I thought.

Then suddenly I am 50 and the shock forces me to run away from another mid-life crisis by buying a yellow campervan and setting off on a tour of the country. I twist my hair into a crazy mess, put on bangles and ankle bracelets and become the hippy I always wanted to be… And for the first time in my life I carry a briefcase. This slightly ruins the look.

The briefcase is full of invitations to visit the homes and gardens of people who helped the National Gardens Scheme raise £2.5million for charities last year and it is for the NGS that I am selflessly treating myself to this indulgent year off. My mission: To use my old VW campervan Daisy to visit people opening their gardens for charity, give them a hand and collect stories along the way for a book. This book.

In my sunshiney Daisybus I meet kind, generous, interesting people, hear inspiring tales of creativity and optimism and learn how gardens are the lifeblood of other people's lives in the same way they are mine. I also eat a lot of cake. Cake and garden visiting go together like strawberries and cream – and sometimes there actually are strawberries and cream available too. Many Garden Owners are also great cake-bakers (I, sadly, am not one of them) and there is nothing so nice and so English as sitting in a garden on a summer's day with tea in china cups and a slice of homemade cake. The spring and summer of 2015 turn out to be epic cake eating seasons for me. 'Quelle hardship' as we say round our house.

Folk wave and smile as the Daisybus and I drive through the spring and summer of 2015. I cover 10,000 miles in six months and am exhausted but wiser and happier when I end the journey in autumn – a journey enlivened and enriched, and sometimes made deeply uncomfortable, by travelling in my lovely old Daisybus.

I have been blessed by the sharing and the laughter of a great many good people. Indeed laughter has been everywhere – even in the company of people who have suffered a great deal – and by the end of this trip I am believing that laughter is as much of a healer as the connection with nature.

No greater personage than His Royal Highness Prince Charles himself describes the National Gardens Scheme as, "one of the happiest fundraising operations this country has known." Each year nearly 4000 gardens are opened to the public through the scheme to allow people to spend a happy hour or two strolling among the flowers with friends, chatting over tea and cake, being inspired, pinching ideas and leaving with renewed excitement about their own patch.

Nature alone can bring great pleasure and peace, but the mix of human creativity and nature that is gardening is, I believe, a recipe for happiness. This is proven to me time and again as I meet people inspired by their gardens – artists, sculptors, musicians and craftsfolk all interconnecting their creativity with nature. Creativity expresses itself in whatever way our DNA will allow. I can't draw, so I use plants to create beauty. Luckily Mother Nature lends a hand – she's like a kind teacher just gently correcting mistakes while I'm out of the class.

What calms us in nature is that we are among things – trees, plants, animals, that are just being themselves. It is a simple message but an enormous lesson to learn and one that is incredibly difficult to absorb for modern humans used to spending their lives desperately chasing that intangible thing called achievement.

Through writing my blog and this book, I continue to meet remarkable people and learn from them and it seems to me that far from being a race alienated from our natural world, we humans know very well what is right for us. Good things and bad have come from our fairly recent industrialisation – we are still children, we're still learning, we're experimenting and travelling a long way from where we started, but I think we're also beginning to feel that we want to come home – and eat cake.

The NGS Head Office Team

Me, layered up ready for a British spring

Prologue

I didn't mean to start in Surrey ... it was my intention to start in Cornwall and follow spring up the country but, as with so much in my life, things don't always go according to plan. And so I found myself darting hither and thither in an attempt to be useful to people, in time for their Garden Open Days. I don't believe I was actually much help, but it was good fun trying.

Being a master of post-rationalisation I can now see that Surrey was exactly where to start – not only is it where I started my life but it's also where the National Gardens Scheme Head Office is based.

Time-travelling down south from my home in Worcestershire in early spring I get to enjoy the flora that hasn't yet come out at home. In the hedgerows, trees and fields a thousand shades of green are starting to show, along with the earliest of blossoms like the blackthorn. (It's good to see, as you near the bottom of your sloe gin supplies, that this year's batch is on its way!)

One of the advantages of driving in the Daisybus is that I get a really good view of people's front gardens (another is that I am higher up than the posh ladies in their four wheel drives – ha!) and it occurs to me that all we are actually doing, in our gardens at this time of year, is painting our own versions of spring. We're copying what we see 'out there' and bringing it closer to home – to where we can enjoy it more intimately, possess it and make it ours. Bringing all that is spread out in nature together into a smaller area concentrates the effect and we get high on the joyful explosion of colour and scent that spring brings us after a dreary British winter. So Spring gardens are essentially miniature portraits of the season. What an exhibition that would make. What gallery would be able to host such a feast?!

Carole's Garden

Although my 'official' start is at the end of March in Surrey, earlier in the spring I'm visiting friends in Cornwall when an invitation comes to visit a garden in Boscastle. Silly not to, thinks I, especially as I love this village, with its wooded valley dropping down to the sea and the pretty whitewashed cottages and National Trust buildings around the harbour. So I now have an excuse to nose around the top half of the village where there is a lovely old place owned by Carole Vincent. Carole's email address makes her sound like some sort of mafia moll – 'ConcreteCarole' – though quite a tough cookie I think, Carole wouldn't waste her concrete on the feet of some poor wretch sent for a 'swim with the fishes' in the Hudson River. She has much more creative plans for it.

Although it is very early spring when I visit it feels like a mid-summer day because I am in a garden with so much interest. The tete-a-tetes must surely be very late, I find myself thinking. Maybe the illusion is helped because I'm by the sea and feel like I'm on holiday, but it is also the style of the garden and the bold use of colour in Carole's own sculptures that make the garden feel fully alive. I immediately decide I must return later in the year to see what high summer is really like here. Any excuse to return to Cornwall, really.

My friends John and Sarah moved near to Padstow (or Padstein as it is sometimes known thanks to the famous chef who has several restaurants there) some years ago and have what appears to be an idyllic life here, totally immersed in the seaside way of life. Their children are all sporty-surfer-dude types and after-school club is basically the beach. If I manage to get DaisyDog in the car to join me she loves the beach as much as me because the big open spaces mean we can play ball properly using the ubiquitous plastic slingers that mean my girl throws can actually cover decent distances. At home my slingerless throws mean the ball arrives in the same place, at the same time as Daisy as she runs ahead to chase it. There is therefore no chase as such and just a disappointed confirmation that the ball has indeed landed. So I think these slingers are quite a brilliant invention. Just about everyone on the beach has one making it quite impossible to tell which dog belongs to which human as balls and dogs fly around recklessly on the sand. I love my walks along the verge of the earth. It seems the waves play with me as I go, pulling me in with the strength of the moon's magnetism. The water gently licks the land, lapping the shore like the edges of pastry being rolled, before returning home to the deep, making shimmering chevrons around stones stuck in sand.

While John cooks supper for us I tell him and his boys about my project and my 1979 VW Type 2 Campervan. Expecting whoops of envy, I am crushed by these cool teenagers telling me surfers don't use those any more – they use Bongos (whatever they are). I suppose 50 really is too late to be considered cool anyway…. Cool is probably not even a cool word any more. I believe 'sick' is cool these days but I can't bring myself to say it and would probably look very uncool if I did, or unsick perhaps?

The boys are equally unimpressed with my vegetarianism and I must admit that refusing to eat fish while you are by the sea does seem a bit churlish. I try to explain to them that it's not that I think humans shouldn't eat animals – I understand the natural food chain – but it is the mass slaughter that I can't abide. I certainly know that if I start talking about the joys of gardening at this point I will go down in history as the most boring person they ever had to meet.

Back in Carole's garden, overlooking Boscastle, I think to myself that surely only a sculptor making it herself, could afford to have such a lot of art in the garden. There is so much stuff to see here it feels like some very sophisticated child has left all their toys outside. I smile to myself as I realise that some of us would say, "No, I shan't put this pot there as it's too close to that one", but in Carol's garden I find several pots next to a concrete bench, next to some concrete balls, next to a concrete table – and it all looks absolutely right. It is right I suppose because it is Carole's garden. It is her art. It is all totally her.

Other gardens must feel so empty to Carol. Every piece she has created for someone else has a double here in her garden; The Armada Dial, commissioned by Plymouth City Council for the city centre; The Devon Pedestrians, commissioned by Devon County Council for town centres in Exeter, Plymouth, Torquay and Barnstaple; The Quartet, for the Royal Scottish Academy of Music and Drama in Glasgow and The Buskers, commissioned by Safeways for Cage Yard, Reigate in Surrey. My favourite though, is the group gathered at the bottom of the garden by a shady pool. They are figures of her friends and Carole says visiting children like to guess what each of them might be thinking.

Carole is inspired by the geology of the earth and the clever colouring she incorporates into the concrete reflects this. To me, her work celebrates the solidity and the intricacy of the very ground we live on and through her art she enables the ground to reach up from the dark towards the light of the sky. There's a lot of vertical gardening alongside the sculpture; last summer's echiums and the beginnings of next and young birches reaching up out of the shade of a pine ready to step into the limelight when the old pine finally gives in to gravity. Concrete columns around the Blue Garden seem so proud to be there with their blue strata exposed and complemented by nearby planting. Far from being unwieldy obstacles in a smallish garden, their presence is bold and somehow reassuring. I feel the garden would be much, much less than it is without them – indeed I feel my own garden is lacking without something so strong and supportive as these structures.

Speaking of strong and supportive, Carol introduces me to her gardener, Jon, who shows me around the wild wood at the top of the garden and introduces me to the concept of dead hedging. Upright sticks and poles hold horizontally laid branches and twigs cleared from the garden and give the look of a layered hedge in winter. I groan inwardly as I think of all that lugging around we have done at home of brash that needed to be 'tidied away'. With a dead hedge around the edge of your property you are never far away from somewhere to put the latest fallen sticks. If only I'd thought of that.

Back with Carole in her blue garden I discover something unique. I'm not sure if this is a one-off but I suspect it might be. Carole made a garden here that then became a Chelsea garden. Sometimes Chelsea show gardens get to have another life after the show, but this part of Carole's garden was here before the show. She simply made a garden she wanted to make and it was so admired that (through the descriptions of an enthusiastic friend) a sponsor, Blue Circle, came forward to take the garden to Chelsea. That was back in 2001 but as I sit here chatting with Carole, it looks just as worthy of a place at Chelsea now.

Carole literally built her home here with her own hands and those same hands have made hundreds of pieces of widely praised concrete art and won her many awards. After a lifetime of art and fifty-three years in this garden, Carole, now 73, thinks maybe she's had enough of concrete and wants to spend more time 'getting the garden right'. There is no doubt in my mind that her love of the earth combined with her artistic talent, will express itself in yet another amazing artwork on the land here in Boscastle. And as

Carole is a long term supporter of the NGS we all get to see it.

I did return later in the year on holiday with my husband and we took along my nephew Theo and his friend Albert. Willy was enchanted and the younger boys declared it to be 'a really cool place'. (Not sick at all.)

David's Garden

In Surrey, on my first 'official' Daisybus visit, David Gold the millionaire owner of West Ham United, tells me how, of all his achievements, including his many businesses which have made him the success he is, the thing that gives him most pride is the restoration of The Chalet and its grounds. He loved the place the first time he saw it – as soon as he drove down through the gates and saw the Cedar of Lebanon ahead of him, he knew that it felt right for him. But there was a lot of work to be done both on the house and the grounds. The place was still covered in fallen trees from the big storm of 1987 and brambles covered them, making a dense, almost impenetrable fallen forest. I guess this is when being a millionaire really helps because assistance in the form of labour and machinery is not the obstacle it might be to the rest of us. However, David does like to get stuck in himself and when time allows he will happily spend a day with his chainsaw cutting back trees and the invasive laurel bushes. As the major clearance work was undertaken daffodils started appearing wherever they could – reaching up after years of dark dormancy for their longed-for breaths of daylight. David, living elsewhere while the house was uninhabitable, describes the joy of arriving one day to a field of daffodils. "Who put those there?" he thought as he drove down the drive. Literally acres of daffodils were liberated and this is why David and his wife Lesley open the garden for the National Gardens Scheme at this time of year.

While I'm there a couple of local journalists, who David obviously knows well, come along to take pictures of David with the Daisybus to help advertise the fact that his garden is open for the NGS this weekend. It all feels slightly surreal to me – millionaire David Gold and owner of a football club, sitting with me in my hippy sunshine bus having our photo taken for the papers. David is clearly totally used to such goings on and is chatting to journalists Julia and Kevin about various other charities that they are all involved in. Speaking of a local one for disadvantaged children, David says, "You can really see how the kids benefit from a day in the garden here". The lucky ones in life are those who can help others and David is one who is fortunate and happy to do that.

This was my first 'interview' and I was woefully bad at it. Hats off to journalists – it's not as easy as it looks. I even forgot to take the simple step of getting my dictaphone out of my handbag and pressing 'Record'. So after I waved goodbye and drove out of sight, I stopped the Daisybus and recorded myself trying to remember all that was said. At the end of the recording my phone rings and I can hear myself saying, "Where's the Pause button? The guy said to use Pause not Stop – Where is Pause? – There is no effing Pause button – He said it was the most important function on it – It's not even here – Hello? (answering the phone) – Jeeeez How do I turn this thing off – No not you, hang on (into my phone) – Aaargh – (I thump OFF instead)

Wendy's Garden

I do remember to switch it on when I get to Wendy Baston's place, the second of my four Surrey visits later that day just three miles away in Warlingham. I sit for a moment or two on the road outside the driveway to the house which rises steeply – really, really steeply to my right. Can the Daisybus make it up that drive or should I leave her here on the road? The only way to do it is with meaning so I rev her up and charge towards the bottom of the slope. I am already committed to the manoeuvre when I wonder whether her front bumper is going to crunch into the first yard of the slope and can only close my eyes and hope for the best. We make it noisily up the slope and find a parking balcony half way up the drive. I've never parked on a balcony before and swing into it rather than tackling the further hill-climb up to the house. Getting out I realise I have left her at an awkward angle between the railings of the balcony and a stone wall behind. I decide to deal with that later and walk up the hill to meet Wendy who provides a welcome coffee, a chocolate biscuit and a garden to recover in.

The recording of this interview is full of our joint pleasure at the beautiful spring afternoon and fresh growth appearing in her garden and a lot of oohing and ahhhing from me about her very nice collection of pots and other interesting accessories placed around the place. Accessorising your garden is a really good way to start gardening and is just how my sister started. Having created a beautiful and stylish home and still having a bit of a shopaholic tendency she started placing 'stuff' outside her back door. Neither a patio or a path or a garden she called it her Outside Back Door

Area which we've shortened to OBDA. "I'm really pleased with my OBDA right now," she'll text and send me a pic of her latest decoration. With the addition of plants to her display of vintage bits and bobs she has created a really pretty space with her OBDA and now she has moved on to the garden proper and has finally caught my gardening bug. "I totally understand now how calming it is," she says. With her husband having been ill and various other stresses in her life she now finds peace in the creative and absorbing process of making her garden. She even writes poems to her garden on a prettily framed blackboard she made and takes gorgeous cameo shots of her work worthy of inclusion in a Country Living feature.

Wendy shows me a collection of old wheels that she bought from a gypsy in Ireland. "I strapped them in the car with the children – luckily their legs were tiny then." I ask about a sculpture of a face with an arm coming out of his eye. "It's from Zimbabwe – He's greeting you" she says, and offers no further explanation.... OK....

On top of the terrace there's some really effective wiggly brickwork that "just evolved" Wendy says and we agree that it's so exciting when you first have a new idea. The 'normal' thing would be to do a straight line but she didn't – where do ideas come from I often wonder..... are they floating around in space waiting for a head to land in?

Wendy would like more ideas to land in her head about keeping deer out of the garden. She shows me a new fence with a young mixed hedge growing in front that will eventually hide it. "Desperate measures – desperate, desperate measures" she repeats. She's tried laser beams, lion poo from the zoo, water pistols. Now they are trying electric fencing. I say that you would never guess there is a deer problem from the appearance of the garden and I admire a group of trees with gorgeous grey leaves "They're Sorbus aria lutescens – we pinched the idea from The Eros Garden at Wisley which has two little dainty chairs and a table in the middle so we kind of adapted it – it's obviously not nearly as nice," she says modestly.

"It's very much not just about the planting with you – there's so much other stuff going on" I observe. I am delighted by a very ordinary archway that Wendy has wound willow around to make quite a beautiful thing indeed – I decide to cover a very cheap and nasty archway of ours in the same way as soon as I get home.

Though not an artist, Wendy's artistic talent shines out in this garden. Every part of the plot has received her thoughtful attention. "The garden has kept me sane and has been a huge and positive addiction for many years," she says.

An extra-long ex-railway bench is complemented by a table made by her husband when she presented him with a plank she 'fell in love with at a sawmill'. It was incredibly heavy but she manoeuvred it herself – we laugh about what you can achieve on your own when you really, really want something "It's called determination" she says. "I had it in the boot with the lid open and drove home with my lights flashing never going over 30mph – it took ages!"

Not afraid to try new things, Wendy has resorted to an 'astro hedge' at the top of the garden where her neighbour cut the hedge over enthusiastically. She's slightly embarrassed about it but actually I really like it as a backdrop – the bright lime green makes the shrubs and tree in front stand out very artistically against it – it looks a bit designery, a bit Chelsea even.

Wendy kindly helps me to do the fifteen point turn required to get out of the balcony. What I don't share with her is the fact that finding reverse on the Daisybus is very much a matter of luck and at this point, right up against the railings twenty feet above the road, I really can't afford to accidentally lurch forward in first gear.

However, it does occur to me that a yellow campervan, crunched on its nose doing a headstand in a polite Surrey avenue, might arguably get more publicity for the NGS than anything else I do. But, thanks to Wendy, I safely roll down her driveway and head off to see a friend in Forest Row before returning to meet my husband Willy for a delicious dinner at the very friendly Whyte Hart in Bletchingley.

Annie's Garden

The next day I meet Annie Keighley who has had a close relationship with the earth since babyhood. Born with hip dysplasia, Annie Keighley spent a lot of her childhood crawling on the ground in her parents' garden in between hospital stays. Perhaps it was the fact that her family were passionate gardeners or the fact that she spent so much time with her hands literally in the soil that she has such greenfingers these days. I immediately notice that in her garden there are pots and pots and pots of cuttings growing happily away. (In my garden there are pots and pots of cuttings rotting away.) I ask her what her secret is and she smiles and tells me that she rubs each cutting between her fingers the way her grandmother showed her before sticking them in pots. Everything takes. That's greenfingers proper.

"So you literally spent your childhood in an intimate relationship with the earth" I say once the niceties are over and Annie tells me her story. "I had my legs in plaster from when I was one and a half 'til I was about five. Quite a lot of the time I actually spent on the ground in the garden because I couldn't walk very much at all. That's probably why I've got this real connection

Quartet in Carole's Garden

Strata Sculpture

Cool Concrete

Me and David Gold in the Daisybus

Annie in the garden ...now and then

Carole's Cornish Garden

with the garden. My grandmother and my aunt used to put me out on the lawn – they used to spend a lot of time in the garden too and I was always around them." She pauses to greet the birds around one of the many feeders full of nuts under a small tree. "My parents had always been keen gardeners and for a long time when I was younger I couldn't do any sporty stuff – that was really quite difficult for me – so my brother and I both had our own plots in the garden and we used to grow cuttings and seeds, which was fantastic."

Annie tells me how it was very traumatic when she was little going through the hospital treatments. "My parents had to leave me behind because in those days we didn't have cars and they used to have to leave me there. So then of course every time I was due to go in to hospital again it became a huge thing. I was so young and I didn't understand. I remember going in and I had my teddy bear with me. The doctor gave me some injections and I was looking down at my knees and I had these plasters – I must have been about two but I remember it really vividly. I was looking to see why I had these plasters on my knees and I asked why. They showed me my teddy bear and my teddy bear had plasters on his knees too. Little things like that have made me remember it really vividly. That was really nice of them."

Annie's problems didn't end in childhood and when I meet her she is recovering from another operation.

"I had this hip problem just after we'd bought the house in 2005. It was a real renovation job" she says (referring to the house not her hips) "because it hadn't been touched since the 50s" and as we sit in her neat and pretty front room Annie tells me the place was uninhabitable when they first bought it. "When Richard and I first came in I went through the floor up to my thighs because the floor just gave way – I was absolutely bruised black and blue." It seems to me her poor legs have been through an awful lot.

"We had three months to get the house done because we had a bridging loan. Both of us were working full time – we used to finish work, come back here, quickly have something to eat and then we'd work 'til twelve o'clock at night and then go back to the old house. One day it was minus three and we were burning the lathe that was falling off the walls to keep warm."

"Had it been empty a long time?" I ask "No," she says, "an old lady had been living in it. The kitchen door was resting on an RSJ and that was the only thing that was holding up the back of the house. When the workmen started coming in all the ceilings fell down because the whole house was shaking as they moved around. It was a real job and a half."

"But we had always loved this house. We used to walk down the gravel pits opposite. We lived on a new estate with a brand new house with a 40' garden which was just too tiny. We used to come past this place and say we really love that house and I wonder who lives there and then one day I was just flicking through property paper and saw it was for sale. So we had to go for it. Once we'd seen the garden we just had to have it."

She shows me photographs of a bramble-filled garden. "The top of the garden was 10' high in brambles and the front garden was just tussocks of grass though the magnolia was there." she says, as I admire the tree currently in its full early spring magnificence.

"Because I've grown up with gardening all my life and we used to move a lot, because my dad used to move around for work, we were always going to new houses and we had to get used to a new garden each time. One of the things we never did was actually rip everything out. We spent time getting a feel for the place which was a really good lesson."

"By the time we moved in here in April things were starting to show. We've kept most of the planting and we brought stuff from the old house too. The house we had we sold to a lady who was just about to have a baby and we had a pond there that she didn't want. She said if we threw the stones in and levelled it off they'd buy the house. So we thought we can't do that because it was really nice stone, so we put all the stone in the back of a friends van and we had two dustbins full of frogspawn and we transported the whole lot here and made a new pond here."

Annie says the whole place has a very special feel to it. "It's a very grounded feel and it's said that there was a medieval sheep dip in the garden here – it's called Sheep Dip Lane – there's this great big monolith outside the house which was part of it. It dates back to the Domesday Book and when we started digging the garden we found stuff like children's leather boots and glass bottles and all sorts of stuff so it must have been used for a long time. I really feel it when I'm in the garden. There is a real sense of peace here."

Like many other gardeners she feels her home and garden have a healing quality. "I don't know what it is but you can go away – I used to work in Slough and had a very frustrating job – and I used to come back here and as soon as I walked through the front door it just goes…. It's one of those places people like to come and stay because they feel kind of calm and peaceful."

I understand this totally. Whilst we are in a busy suburban area of Surrey this garden is a haven. New housing estates surround this ancient cottage and it seems to sit quite happily amongst them –like a great, great grandmother sitting quietly among her rowdy offspring at her 100th birthday party – smiling gently and contentedly in the knowledge that all is well in this little patch of Earth.

Annie tells me she feels really strongly about living alongside nature in the garden. "One of the best things for me was, when I got very down and very depressed, we got a summerhouse – I've got electric in here and in the summer we open the doors up and have the parasol out here and have fairy lights." I do actually have severe summerhouse envy and Annie tells me of a lady who rang her and said she had been so inspired by her summerhouse that she'd had her own built and invited Annie to come for tea. "It's so nice when you inspire other people isn't it? she says. "I can sit in here with a book and it's like a bird hide because the birds come" she says beaming "You get the great tits coming down and the blue tits coming down and the coal tits and blackbirds and collared doves." And she says it makes her think about what we're putting in our gardens. "People laugh at me and say slug pellets won't hurt the birds – they try to convince me that they won't do any harm but I'd rather not risk it. Last year I used a bug spray and none of the blue tits came. It was supposed to be organic but it changed the whole ecosystem." Annie is happy to let nature take its course and problems sort themselves out. "People ask why we haven't got any blackfly and I say well the blue tits eat them of course."

Annie understandably became downhearted when she had an operation that didn't go well "I found that I could hardly move and I got really frustrated because I found I couldn't do stuff." But nothing was going to stop Annie gardening…. "I got really lucky with the physios – who were amazing" she says, "they said 'Right what do you want to do in the garden?' My physio was laughing at me – she said 'What is it you can't do?' So I said well I can't get out of the bed once I'm in there. She said 'Well show me what you do normally', so I showed her – stepping backwards trying to get through the bushes. She said 'Well nobody could do that!' She thought I had ridiculously high aims but they literally worked out steps for me. They put things in the borders to help me because I used to go into the borders and then I couldn't get out again" she laughs "I was shouting for Richard to get me out! I have no propulsion so it is really hard to get up after you've gone down. But now I've got obelisks and trees that I can use to pull myself around and stones so I can feel where to place my feet. And I've got raised beds too. I do most of the gardening and I'm on top of it," she says. I love the fact that plant supports double as Anne supports – it really is a harmonious garden.

Like me Anne says she's learned most of her gardening 'by osmosis' but she still has a desire to learn more and more.

"I used to work at Marylyn Abbott's West Green House Gardens on Thursdays and one of the things I learned there was about succession. The way they keep their garden going is that the greenhouse provides succession plants. They always have stuff in the greenhouse ready to go out, so as soon as something has faded in the borders they're digging up and replacing with new stuff. We used to do a lot of sculpting in the borders too, so I got good practice at pruning. Marylyn was great; she used to invite you to chat about planning the next borders. I really miss that now. But I had a nasty fall in July – I slipped in the garden centre and that has set me back again."

With all this bad luck you might think Annie would be feeling a bit sorry for herself, but she shows no sign of self-pity at all. "When I was getting ready for the last operation, I couldn't do the stuff I was doing before, so I enrolled for an RHS Level 2 Horticulture Course. It was a bit hard doing the practicals but I did the theory and I passed all the exams. I'm hoping to get to the point where I can do the practicals too."

Becoming absorbed in something is such a good way of coping with difficult times I say. Annie replies, "Yes, it's really interesting because I did it just because I wanted to learn. Richard is very good with the Latin names but my parents aren't good at that. They are fantastic gardeners – they are totally besotted with gardening – they actually fitted up ark-lights so they can carry on gardening after dark! They both love gardening and they're still gardening at over 90 now. It's a huge sweep of garden."

I admire Annie for her eagerness to keep learning. I agree with her that I would like to know my subject better – more intimately. Alas I know that I suffer from a pathetic lack of stamina so there is really no point in me signing up to do a course. But there was another bonus to further education for Annie too "The people on the course were so lovely. They were all changing the direction of their lives. One of them was a nurse. One had a very unhappy marriage and wanted to start out on her own. Everybody had a different reason for doing the course. Some of us are still in touch. It was lovely because we were such like-minded people we got on so well – it was fantastic."

Annie makes it sound so nice that I find myself tempted again to sign up, "Even if you were having a hard time people were really kind and study groups formed and people went to see gardens together. It was really nice. It was a really good thing to do and because I couldn't do anything else, I was captive and so I made use of that time."

When people started asking to take photographs of her garden, Annie decided she would too – to give her another way of looking at the garden. She says in a photograph you spot things that don't look quite right. She enjoys the new hobby so much that her brother gave her some photography lessons in exchange for some gardening and now she's the Publicity Officer for the NGS in Surrey and gets to visit lots of other lovely gardens in the county to take media shots. "Thursday is my NGS day, so I see behind the scenes and I just love that."

No time-waster our Annie! And admirably organised too. "I always keep garden journals where I put the things I'm doing. Every year we plan out the vegetable beds so it is all done on a rotation system. And so when I was convalescing I was planning what would go in and did loads of reading of gardening books."

Apparently Annie's husband Richard used to think gardening was for pensioners but he was always interested in growing vegetables. "We had a long thin garden once where he made terraces – he likes the hard landscaping. His Dad used to show sweet peas and Richard used to help him with the exhibits. He does garden but he is very scientific the way he does stuff. He's quite competitive too!"

Annie truly believes her garden has helped her healing process. "I think I would have given up actually without it" she says, and points to the fresh growth of some beans "That is the sort of thing – seeing things grow – the first time you see your beans coming up." We laugh about growing potatoes when they are as cheap as chips in the shops (we laugh again at my accidental pun) "It's when you turn the soil over and find those first golden nuggets – it's so exciting!" Annie is quite allergic to lots of food "so we grow what we eat, she says, "I think that's a big part of the connection too."

Walking slowly around her garden I notice that she plants a bit like me – saying to plants "Budge up everyone! There's room for one more." But in Annie's garden they all seem to be muddling happily along and not suffering for the cosiness. There is some inspiring planting too. I leap on the idea of white thalias coming up with the early maroon lysimachia leaves, because once you've got the maroon lysicmachia, as we have, you've got it for life and it actually isn't that pretty a plant with its yellow flowers. "I keep cutting it because I hate the yellow flowers" Annie says, echoing my thoughts. "After the Thalias I've got white penstemon coming up which looks nice with the purple foliage." Another one for my notebook: Use white flowers to go with purple foliage – keep cutting foliage. Why didn't I think of that?

While I'm writing Annie disappears to the kitchen asking if I would like some pear tart. "Sounds amazing" I say and it is. I fear I will be enormous by the end of my trip if everyone feeds me like this. I leave with my already too small vintage hippy trousers (bought especially to match the Daisybus) feeling even tighter and with huge admiration for a lady who has been through a lot of pain but whose great love of nature and gardening appears to see her through pretty much anything.

My last visit in this area is to Sunshine Residential Care Home in Weybridge – the first care home to open its garden for the NGS. The garden is a safe place for residents to spend time outside and I am shown around by Nicola Mercer who tells me, "The garden has raised beds for easy access and to make it easy to touch, smell and see the plants. It's a tranquil safe space with lots of seating" (and it's very inviting plush and comfy seating I am thinking...) "Some of the residents have dementia which is essentially like being a child again – there is a sandpit so they can enjoy the feel of the sand and soil and the sensory planting in the Reminiscence Garden brings back memories through smell and colour. In the summer there is a garden club and the residents are quite excited about opening the garden for the NGS."

I talk to Mimi, one of the residents. In her beautiful strong Italian accent she tells me she doesn't work in the garden herself but advised the bosses to get two old boys and give them half the garden each to look after "Zis way zey will compete to make it better than the other boy's – zat would make the garden look really good" she says! I like Mimi and spend some time with her hearing lots of stories not about gardening before she tires of me and moves off to talk to someone else.

A few days later when the weather has reverted to winter again as it does, infuriatingly, in March, I am on the motorway heading towards Derbyshire. One thing I hadn't thought through properly – well at all really – is that I would have to spend so much time on motorways, dual carriageways and bypasses. I had had an image of sunshine and coastal roads, blue skies and country lanes. My sister calls this my Pollyanna take on life and I admit I didn't give much thought to how I would get to such idylls from Worcestershire. On this wet day in March I have my first experience of the Daisybus being blown sideways across the lanes of the motorway and Pollyanna is brought down to earth. I vow this will be the last time I drive on a motorway in an old campervan. DaisyDog is hating every minute as much as me – and the thought of my arrival at my destination in Derbyshire doesn't cheer me much as tonight we're camping. With no heater. Hey Ho.

Craig's Garden

When I arrive at The Burrows Garden, Nicky Dalton straight away insists that I spend the night in the house so DaisyDog and I immediately love her. "There's no way I can let you sleep out there on a night like this" she says. Daisy introduces herself to the dog of the house and steals his place by the fire. With a glass of wine in my hand and my bum on a soft sofa, we have made ourselves well and truly at home within about ten minutes.

As baby Ana sits happily watching the appropriate and charming 'In The Night Garden' Nicky tells me how she is coping having been left alone with her daughter after losing Craig so suddenly and unexpectedly. He simply went to bed grumbling about a cold one January night and collapsed on the bathroom floor. My heart breaks for her as she tells how she misses him and their new happy family life.

Nicky and I share our tales of woe, veering off into laughter over shared thoughts now and then. For her, like me, a sense of humour is sometimes the only way through. And it was, amongst other things, a sense of humour that she shared with her husband Craig who particularly enjoyed urging visiting county ladies to 'Come and see my balls' while innocently gesturing to the rows of immaculately topiarised privet lollipops in his garden full of structure and grandeur. I ask whether it is his sense of humour that installed the gold encrusted, very grand iron archways in the garden of a large, but not-very-grand farmhouse, but Nicky says, "No – he just liked the bling." But they are also there because Craig was a great fan of talented craftsmen. As well as the arches, obelisks and plant supports are very much a feature of the garden in their own right and testament to the skills of the local artists.

The garden is immaculate. As I open the curtains of the guest bedroom in the morning I wonder what on earth I can do to help – even on our best days our garden comes nowhere near the perfection below me. Nicky tells me, "That's how Craig left it – he liked things to be neat – he wasn't someone to leave the tidying up 'til spring." This has been a godsend as Nicky says she knows nothing about gardening and as well as everything else, she has to somehow cope with not one but SIX Open Garden dates that Craig offered the NGS. They're in print in the famous Yellow Book so cancelling might still mean some people will turn up and Nicky has decided that anyway she wants to do Craig proud and show his creation in the way he would have wanted.

It's hard not to shed tears in sympathy as it really sinks in that in the first month of this year she has become a widow, a single mother and a gardener. None of which she was expecting. I am praying to myself that the garden will be her salvation in the way it was mine – and that at the very least, with her determination to continue with the six Open Days, she will have plenty to keep her busy.

I ask Nicky to show me around starting with the bits she is worried about. The first thing I notice is that there is nothing to worry about. Craig has left it pretty much ready for the first Open Day in April.

Even without a flower showing (a few daffodils here and there) the garden is a beautiful place to be and graceful too (even with the bling). Wide lawns are flanked with structure of plant or iron and fresh spring growth is popping up in the weed-free borders. A colonnade of white stone has great heaps of hebe leading up to it, making all the difference to a design often seen. "Craig loved structure, trees and hydrangeas," Nicky says. And it is only the hydrangeas that need attention. Nicky has left their heads on being aware that they help protect from frost, but (after a quick phonecall to my friend and garden guru Tamsin Westhorpe) I confirm that it is now safe to take them off and we set about a pleasant morning beheading hydrangeas and revealing the lovely fat juicy shoots bursting with new life.

Hail storms interrupt us now and again and I shelter under a laurel bush with a blue plastic bucket over my head and pull the Daisy Dog under it with me. It's just a passing shower we assure ourselves. But with the third extended shower we admit defeat and I bundle one Daisy into another and sadly head for home.

I need all my strength to deal with the gale-force winds and gusts from passing lorries on the roads home and daffodils that danced happily a week ago in Surrey are now pogo-ing like angry punks from my youth on the way home. I feel like joining them – angry in the way you are when you feel unable to help someone out of their misery. No-one's at fault – it's just another reminder that life just isn't fair and I want to kick something with my Doc Martens.

When I started this project I hoped I might be able to visit perhaps a dozen gardens so it was a great surprise to receive invitations to around four hundred! What has been lovely has been the variety of gardens. I have been as likely to visit a tiny plot at 3a Church Street as to visit The Old Rectory, a grand country pile or a horticultural business. Being fairly ignorant I suppose, I didn't recognise names that perhaps I should – like David Gold – and so I arrived at most destinations with absolutely no preconceptions at all. David's house is called The Chalet so before I realised who he was I imagined a check shirted forester in a nice modest little wooden cabin in the woods somewhere.

Admittedly The National Gardens Scheme started with the great and good opening their large country gardens to the public to raise money for charity, and thank goodness that tradition continues. But today the NGS welcomes anyone who has a garden of interest – their main aim being to raise money for charities rather than to create a network of 'elite gardens'. It is nonetheless flattering to be accepted into the scheme and something I would encourage everyone to do if they possibly can. If you are passionate about your garden it is probably something other people would like to see. It doesn't have to be grand, just well done and interesting. If it is small you can get together with neighbours or create a local garden trail and these days there are a lot of people combining a garden opening with some other interest like art or crafts. One garden I visited had a display of model ships. Combining an art exhibition for example, with a garden opening extends the invitation to people who would perhaps normally choose to visit a gallery rather than a garden so this can only be good for the NGS and their charities as it extends the appeal.

In any case, if you don't want to open your garden you are still helping all the charities by visiting the gardens and there are so many selfish reasons for doing this too. I love them if they're gorgeous and give me ideas to pinch; if they're really peaceful and I just enjoy being there; and I also really enjoy it when someone has got more weeds than me and I can feel ever so slightly smug. And I know for sure that getting people into gardens soon encourages them to have a go themselves and this is my great passion: more gardeners = more happy people = a better world. This is my simple recipe for world peace.

Paul's Garden

In World War II Paul Willan's father served with the Gurkhas and found himself falling in love with rhododendrons in the Himalayas. I think of him as an opportunistic plant hunter making the best of things in a very British way. He and his Italian wife developed a number of their own unique hybrids back here in England and Paul still cares for the plants in his parents' garden (now his and Jeannie's garden) in Cheshire.

As I drive into Cheshire the county sign welcomes me with the announcement that Cheshire is "The Home of Britain's Finest Gardens" and I can't help but feel a little indignant as I would say Herefordshire has Britain's finest gardens. Of course I am biased. Not only do I live on the border but I also help run the Herefordshire Horticultural Hub which has brought together a lovely bunch of people from the local horticultural scene in The Marches area. We do indeed have some pretty amazing gardens, but then I realise with Arley Hall, Cholmondeley Castle and Tatton Park, Cheshire have possibly got a point. They've certainly got lots of big ones and some quirky ones too that I'd like to visit like Poulton Hall – a storyteller's garden.

Cheshire is kind of big all over really I think as I drive around looking for the right street. It's well known for its rich and famous footballers and the beautiful ladies darting from Landrover to hairdresser, Porsche to nail salon look immaculate and expensive. It's what my grandmother would call a very 'well-to-do' area and Paul, who is a solicitor, has a large and elegant house on a street full of large and elegant houses. But my interest is the garden and the fact that this 'des res' is surrounded by some beautiful choice specimen plants. At the entrance Paul has planted some giant bamboo, which rustle pleasingly and muffle the noise from a road liberally sprinkled with large luxury cars.

To a garden with an impressive and unique variety of rhododendrons so lovingly assembled by his parents, Paul is adding his own particular favourites – peonies of all kinds. With the rhodies bringing the garden to life early in the year, the peonies follow on in an equally impressive way. I find peonies the most joyful of flowers. They are the big romantic blousy queens of the garden. They are Barbara Cartland flowers. Their massive heads of dozens of frilly petals just sing summer to me. I have long been trying to achieve a gobsmacking peony bed to take the breath away and inspire gasps of admiration from my garden visitors, but my usual impatience has meant that I have given them too much competition to thrive and added too much else to the border resulting in a fairly disastrous display of weedy peonies, weedy roses and weedy sedums. I will learn. Slowly.

Paul tells me of his interest in Japanese gardens while he cooks us a tasty lunch and I spend a very pleasant spring afternoon weeding with him in his garden. In truth I fear I was a disappointment, as Paul joins me on my side of the garden and comments how well I have carefully weeded around the moss. I love moss and never remove it – I think it's lovely ground cover and encourage it at home but Paul laughs and says he has too much. The grass (or moss) is always greener isn't it? I wish I could roll it up like a carpet and take it home with me.

Jane's Garden

This is the early days of my tour and I soon realise that I need to organise myself better as I am flitting around from Cornwall to Surrey to Derbyshire to Cheshire, back home to a book signing by my friend and herb expert Kim Hurst then Oxfordshire and now Bath within two weeks. I chastise myself for my very bad planning especially as it is expensive on fuel and emissions.

Today I make things even worse by refusing to use the motorway and aiming for Jane Neech's address near Bath on A and B roads. However, it is a very beautiful journey – what a lovely area of rolling hills and pretty villages! And today they're looking especially beautiful in the sunshine and the bright greens and blues of spring greenery and sky. Somehow I end up in Glastonbury where a blockage in the road means the traffic is having to do U-turns in the High Street with traffic parked on both sides. U-turns are particularly difficult in the Daisybus and require all my strength to pull the steering wheel round only to achieve an inch or so in the available space. I am initially anxious about executing the manoeuvre in front of a street full of shoppers but as I look up I see that everyone is smiling kindly at me and helping me turn so that in the end I feel as though I have actually been the centre of some lovely vintage hippy dance – more of a twirl than an U-turn – and I'm aware I am blushing but grinning happily as everyone waves me off. My red face hottens because although the Daisybus has no heater as soon as the sun shines she warms up quickly because of all the glass and today I get hotter and hotter with my layered clothing difficult to remove without stopping. I can't stop because I'm late.

Finally arriving and having been settled with a cool drink in Jane's garden she tells me that her parents were also keen gardeners and as Jane herself married another gardener it is perhaps not surprising that their daughter Gemma is now a highly qualified horticulturalist working with the modern-day plant hunter Tom Mitchell at Evolution Plants near Bath.

I enjoy helping Jane in her garden as the day gets warmer, though I'm slightly nervously feeling that I have the eyes of three generations of gardeners watching over me. The garden is beautifully looked after and has obviously had a lot of thought put into it but also welcomes the surrounding countryside with breaks and 'windows' in the hedging offering views beyond. 'Borrowed scenery' is always a great idea so long as you're not next door to a factory. Back home I love the contrast of my garden next to a field of sheep. I never know which is actually more idyllic: my garden with its huge variety of plants, teaming with wildlife or the simple grass meadow beyond with nothing but grazing sheep.

I help Jane with planting in the shady area underneath the trees by the back door. "The bamboo is doing well but I want more vegetation – I want to create an area where we sit" she says, but laughs, "it's very much a working garden – we don't sit in it much!" Near the bamboo there is a very old Clematis montana with wonderful thick twisty stems. Most of the flowering growth is at the top so Jane has simply planted another young one to grow up through the old. A brilliant idea methinks : clematis growing up clematis! I make a mental note to copy that idea. There are many gorgeous clemmies in this garden – as I walk around I see more and more – and Jane says she is very pleased with them now, although pigeons used to take the tops out. "The pigeons aren't so much of a problem now we have cats." I make another mental note to justify my numerous cats as clematis saviours to my husband.

It soon becomes apparent that Jane and I are not at all alike – in the gardening sense. I am chaotic and Jane is a perfectionist – one of her favourite tools is the power washer. "When I wash the patio it shows the fossils in the natural stone." she explains. I wonder what might be exposed if I power-washed our paths. Best not to think really. Jane shows me her White Border and we discuss how successive planting is very tricky. It looks to me like she's got the knack though with hellebores followed by snowdrops then tulips, alliums and lupins. "But" she says, "it's lacking in autumn." I say that I think garden visitors understand that it is very difficult to have one border looking brilliant all year and as extra consolation I also tell her of my belief that perfect borders can put off beginners because they think they'll never be able to achieve it. To me the point is the gardening – the process – not the finished product. But I'm not convincing Jane.....

"But I am a perfectionist!" she says, "so it is hard when people come round and it's not perfect." I suggest some white sedum for the autumn and feel pleased that Jane likes the idea and that in some small way I may have finally contributed to 'Perfection'.

"We had some Japanese visitors in November" Jane continues "We were panicking, thinking 'Gosh, what is the garden going to look like in November?' But fortunately it was a dry day and do you know? They absolutely loved it. They loved the summerhouse, the greenhouses (we have his and her greenhouses!), the compost – they wanted to see the whole package – not necessarily the plants." Like Paul in Cheshire, Jane is interested in Japanese gardening too. "Their gardens are very spiritual and you could say our garden is a spiritual place in a different way. We can learn a lot from the way the Japanese think about balance and alignment."

Jane tells me more about her daughter's embarkation on a career in horticulture. After a degree in Plants Sciences, Gemma then did a Masters in Horticulture and did her dissertation while working at the nursery at Evolution Plants. "Tom used to be a banker so he values people more and pays quite well" she tells me, "but jobs in horticulture are not well paid generally" Jane is happy that her daughter is working in something she loves and we both wonder if maybe there is a movement towards lifestyle being more important than wealth to young people. I do hope so.   Since my visit Gemma has been appointed Horticultural Team Leader at RHS Wisley and made her parents even more proud of her achievements.

TWIGS

After a couple of weeks visiting beautiful homes and beautiful gardens I am excited to visit TWIGS in Swindon – An amazing place where people can overcome all sorts of disadvantages and illnesses through community horticulture.

I realise I don't know much about Swindon as I travel towards it, apart from the infamous Magic Roundabout. Built in 1972 at a time when I was watching a gentler version with Florence and Zebedee, it consists of five mini-roundabouts arranged around a sixth central, anti-clockwise roundabout. I anticipate some angry beeping as I sail around this, what some call iconic, road junction. Satnav Shirley can't keep up when I'm driving around lots of roundabouts so I'm just hoping the signage is good. (Shirley is so named after the number of times I say "Surely not?" when she instructs me to take an unlikely looking turning.)

Sometimes driving the Daisybus feels more like sailing than driving. I don't know if it's the size of her or that her engine is in the back while I'm at the bow but the sensation is particularly strong while swinging around roundabouts. It would be enjoyable if it wasn't accompanied so often with hoots of impatience from other motorists who actually know which way they are going. I cringe as I imagine irate drivers ringing Head Office at the NGS to complain about my driving, but I comfort myself with the fact that if they have noticed the NGS signs in the window then that's actually A Good Thing.

Alan Holland is the energetic force that steers 'Therapy Work In Gardening, Swindon'. I fall on him as guru, expert and proof of my theory that gardening can help and heal anyone.

"It is a real growth area – excuse the pun," he says, "Wellbeing has become a real key word. Everyone is talking about wellbeing, mental health and a holistic approach"

"I think this is an aspect of gardening that more and more people are looking to benefit from. There's a feeling of 'Hang on a minute, I could be a bit happier if I did this.'" Alan tells me how Swindon is involved in an initiative called the Five Ways to Wellbeing, a national campaign to; Connect, Take Notice, Keep Learning, Be Active and Give. "We believe that everyone needs to be able to connect on these five levels to maintain or gain wellbeing." Alan explains.

I tell Alan that often people I meet describe gardening to me as calming, relaxing, and soothing. Even the harder work is described as therapeutic – people dig when they're feeling angry or frustrated, prune and even chop down trees as a stress-releasing exercise. Some people take to me to one side and say quietly to me "You know, I find it's very good if you're feeling a little down or (whispered) depressed". There is still some unnecessary shame attached to feeling depressed but so many people suffer from depression in this country, especially in the winter months, including me. I tell Alan that my depression is far worse in the winter and I'm sure that is because I'm not outside gardening and he says, "Yes, SAD syndrome is very real – lots of people come here who need the light to help them get through the winter."

Alan and I agree that when we're going through hard patches and we're a bit down, the idea of doing the garden is sometimes too much. "You just think I can't do it, I don't want to do it. And yet as soon as you do start doing it, you feel better." We agree that although being outside is good in itself, just sitting in a garden sometimes is not as helpful to the mind as doing something in a garden. "It's almost a symptom of being unwell in your mind – your inability to be creative," says Alan. Spending time outside really does help – if you can get yourself out there in the first place!

Organisations such as the mental health charity Mind are ensuring that talking about mental wellbeing is becoming normal and very soon, I hope, there will be no taboo to deal with, as well as the tangle of knots inside our heads. Hopefully in future, people won't feel they have to whisper to me their feelings about nature helping their depression.

Alan tells me that people get referred to TWIGS in a range of ways – "Many people come from CPN (Community Psychiatric Nurses) and people who are engaged in the mental health services, as well as GPs and other organisations such as drug and alcohol services. People can self-refer to us but over the years, especially since the government has played around with benefits, we get referrals from the Job Centre. A lot of long-term unemployed also have a form of mental health problem through feeling under-valued and not feeling a part of society. They can become reclusive."

Most people are happy to attend TWIGS but Alan says they do occasionally have issues with resistance. "Some people are told they have to spend time here – they're told 'you have to attend or else you'll will lose your benefits'. Subsequently, some people come down and they're very open about the fact that they don't really want to be here. We say 'Look, if you're not motivated to do this we can't help you.'"

Alan goes off to give direction to one of the volunteers who is taking the long, whippy growth out of an apple tree. I follow him to the orchard where he tells me, "When we came on this site the only things here were fruit trees – a square of apple and pear trees. They'd been planted by different schools because it was owned by the council – it was their amenity horticulture site. Then they sold it off and got contractors in. The garden centre was built and this was set aside as a community project. These trees hadn't ever been pruned and we're trying bit by bit to get them down to a manageable shape and size."

"You need to keep the centre open and keep the fruit on reachable branches," he explains to the volunteer.

Apart from the fruit trees, Alan inherited the proverbial 'blank canvas' so everything I see has evolved in the last 16 years. It is the most uplifting place I've ever visited. The garden is split into different areas, where people work on different projects either alone or with others. Alan shows me the individual garden plots "People can redevelop and design their own space. Sometimes two people come together and they look through the gardening books in the unit and come up with a plan."

The individual gardens are manageable at 10'x20' "So if someone is coming to only one session a week they can still make a difference and feel in control, but there is always work that needs doing in the larger garden too."

As I look around I am so motivated by what Alan and everyone else is doing here that I not only want to get stuck into the garden there and then, but want to move to Swindon so I can become a permanent part of this positive place. If I live here I am bound to find a short cut to avoid the roundabout.

Alan is continuing, "We have a communications slot first thing in the morning when everyone is here. One of the staff will have gone round the gardens and written down a whole list of jobs and then we offer it out to people and they choose what they'd like to do. Some people want to work on their own and others definitely want to work as part of a team. It's about giving choice and variety and trying to keep them motivated."

Then Alan takes me to the thatched round house built by staff and volunteers using wattle and daub for the walls that they made in the traditional way, with soil dug from the ground mixed with straw, cow manure and lime. Alan says, "We used to have a covering of reeds on the inside roof but local youths pulled it all out. We fundraised thousands to put up fencing but we've still got two vulnerable sides." But Alan says, "We don't mind sharing if they're respecting the place. It's a lovely, soothing, quiet place here and on the hottest summer's day it always stays cool. Lots of people were involved in the building but initially it came from a young man in his 20s who was referred to us. He was doing an art degree, went off the rails, got heavily into drink and drugs and had a complete melt-down. He was sectioned into Swindon's in-patient unit and then he was referred on to us. When he came to us he was totally demotivated – didn't want to do any of the gardening. So I said, 'Well, is there anything you **would** like to do?' 'I'd quite like to build a roundhouse,' he said. So I said OK and he started doing sketches and he gradually sold the idea to lots of people. He said 'it won't take hardly any money, we can use recycled materials….' so we gave him a spade and said, 'You can build one here'. So he started digging and people joined him and it started growing. He enthused about 20 volunteers and on our books we've got up to 80 people a week who come for sessions, so people would just come and join in with him. He became better in himself and started getting himself back together again, and actually he left before we finished doing the roof because he got back on an art degree course and came out with a very good degree. He then went on to set himself up with a Business Enterprise Award as a ceramicist

in Wales. The last we heard he'd got a job as Head of Ceramics at a university. He came back on one of our open days and saw the finished roundhouse and was quite emotional."

Next Alan shows me The Faith Garden built with Swindon Interfaith Group. I admire some artwork I don't really understand: "It's a Hindu symbol for one-ness made here in the craft section," he tells me. "Six different faith groups came together with their ideas of what was important to their faith and how that could be incorporated into the garden and we went out to the community and people from different faiths decorated 108 pebbles that went into a path. The path is significant to three of the faiths. Other people from other groups came here to help build the garden. It was a really nice project."

By this time I can hardly contain my excitement about this place and start having grandiose dreams of ensuring there is a TWIG in every town in the country.

Meanwhile, Alan is told 'The Duck Man has arrived' and I make a few notes about what I've seen so far while they discuss the forecast for weekend which will affect the success of the annual Duck Race organised by Swindon Rotary group. The Duck Man has a big digger with a big bucket on it. It's a simple plan – people pay their money to get a duck with a number on it which goes into the bucket and then they tip the bucket in the river and the ducks 'race'. 50p per duck goes to TWIGS. I'm liking this place more and more.

Next we visit the Crafts studio "Crafts are a popular part of the project, the opportunity to express one's creativity leads to a greater sense of wellbeing," says Alan "A lot of people say when they first come here that they either don't believe they've got creative abilities or they have had, but, because of their depression or other mental health issues, their self-confidence has hit rock bottom and they've lost motivation. We will then show them around the site and we'll be pointing out pieces of work others have created, and they'll say 'O I could never make anything like that' and then a few months down the line there they are turning out something fantastic."

While being very much a place for people, Alan tells me the organic management of the whole garden takes wildlife into account too. "We've had a lot of butterflies already this year and if people are interested in bees they can get involved with the Swindon & District beekeepers who keep bees here."

There is also a designated wild area, The Haven, run by John Ball specifically to encourage butterflies. "John is planting native species that he knows are part of the life-cycle of certain butterflies and moths. He's passionate about butterflies – his charity is FAB (Flowers And Butterflies) and his mission statement is to make Swindon the butterfly capital of Europe."

It appears I have still only seen a small part of the set up here. Alan points to the side of a lake. "We have the use of a small field where we grow concentric circles of willow varieties which we coppice every winter and use the withies to make hurdles and plant supports. On the other side of the lake we have a large organic allotment site – 14 allotment plots – which are shared with another charity called DASH (Discovering Autistic Spectrum Happiness). They work with people with Aspergers and run sessions every Wednesday."

We meet some visitors to the site and talk about how daffodils make you smile. I've yet to meet someone who doesn't like daffodils. Alan warns the visitors not to get in the bee flight path as another visitor just had a close encounter with a swarm. But Alan says, "When they're swarming you're unlikely to get stung because they're all about protecting the queen – it's best to just keep still while they pass. When beekeepers go to collect a swarm the prime aim is to get the queen in the box – as soon as you can get her inside all the others will follow."

School groups also get referred to TWIGS, Alan tells me. "The children do a range of tasks around the site. Every Wednesday we have a group of children with emotional and behavioural problems that have been taken out of the normal curriculum to do activities like this as part of their wellbeing. The school system, 'one size fits all', doesn't work for everyone. But they love it here. They do seasonal activities – whatever we're doing – pruning trees and planting. It's important not to make it too mysterious – make gardening easy to do – accessible. We are only facilitators of the growth after all."

Next I'm shown the woodworking area. "We go out and work in local woodlands for the Forestry Commission and Woodland Trust, we work on the old railway between Swindon and Marlborough which is the SUSTRANS cycle route. When we work in the woodland we get to bring back fresh timber and we have a pole lathe as part of this area where volunteers are able to turn the timber into useable products."

I love the connections that Alan has made with different organisations – pulling everyone together for the common good and inviting the general public to join in too through Friends of TWIGS. "We've had willow working and felt-making workshops and we brought in a medicinal herbalist who ran some workshops for us here, helping people to look at how they might possibly have a life without lots of dependency of synthetic drugs." And Alan says people were so interested in the herbal workshops that they asked if they could make their own Physic Garden. "Originally it was just plants that we knew had a beneficial effect on our mental wellbeing and then over time it has drifted to include any plant that we know is good for our health. The herbalists' treatment is all about a holistic approach – so you wouldn't just take St Johns Wort to treat depression, you would look at taking a range of plants that treated the whole body." We both crush some lemon balm leaves nearby and Alan tells me that they are brilliant for treating tension headaches. "Make some tea with them – it really works."

With birdsong in the bushes nearby we then walk along The Path of Life, put together by a group of people who came up with the concept of a garden representing the journey through their illness. It starts with a barren, bleak area with a sad and beautiful sculpture of a crouching child. Alan tells me, "It's called 'Despair' – it represents how one of our volunteers came down and found his son one morning. Gradually, as you go up the path the planting begins to brighten and on the stones are mosaics that say 'One Step At A Time'. A really important element is that there is an escape at the end of the garden so you don't have to come back down through the bleak bit. Sometimes we use this when people first come to us. We ask them where they think they are on the path."

Some very strange-looking contraptions turn out to be Outside Fitness Stations. "We were given a grant to install six of these around the site, following research about the 'Green Gym' approach, which showed that if you exercise in a green environment it is better for you."

In the greenhouses and polytunnels I'm introduced to volunteers pricking out young plants. Alan says, "It's great that, because this is such a rewarding and therapeutic activity there are always people here to see that this work gets done and the plants do really well." In here they also grow seasonal crops like tomatoes and peppers and much of this ends up in the lovely Olive Tree café that has been set up in the garden centre next door by people who used to work at TWIGS. "The café provides opportunities for work for people with mental health problems and other disabilities. Quite a lot of the paid staff are people who started off as volunteers. It's a really popular, busy café. We share the kitchen garden to produce salad crops and fruits for the café. Recently we were given some money to set up some cut flower gardens and we're going to grow a whole range of cut flowers and sell bunches in the café."

By this time I honestly cannot think of anywhere else I would rather work than this amazing place. I find out that the garden is open Mondays, Wednesdays and Fridays for gardening sessions and the gardens are used for other events too. "We hold a Spring and a Summer event and then two NGS days in between" Alan says, and I say that it must be a surprising oasis for people to find in the middle of an industrial estate in Swindon. "Yes, the Open Days do very well – 1000 people if the weather is good and they know they can buy things like the bird boxes and our plants. The NGS brings in a different group of visitors to our own Open Days. I would dearly like to see the NGS including a mental health charity in their list of beneficiaries" he says, smiling.

Coming to the end of my tour, Alan stops by a little quince tree and says, "Gosh that's looking the best I've seen it for years" to a lady standing quietly by. It turns out that Mary spotted it looking rather sick and sad and felt sorry for it, so she decided it would be her project and she has been feeding it and weeding around it and giving it some TLC and has managed to successfully nurture it back to health. And this seems to me to be the perfect analogy for TWIGS itself. What Mary has received from TWIGS she has passed on to the quince. Alan tells me it is a simple case of Biophilia which is a word that is new to me (but I have used a lot since).

He explains, "Biophillia is our inert connection to nature and we as a species have been losing it – especially in the western world. We can't be truly happy unless we have a connection to nature. As you know there is proven research. Being connected to a computer all day isn't good for us – being connected to nature is."

On my way home I reflect on what I've seen today and recall reading research that showed simply lying on the ground on a summer's day and placing your hand on bare soil has its own simple value. This is partly because we are just being still in fresh air, but also because free electrons that are emitted from the earth are natural antioxidants so I guess it's therefore a kind of lazy detox.

Research shows that direct physical contact with the vast supply of electrons on the surface of the Earth promotes physiological changes and subjective reports of wellbeing. Earthing (or grounding) refers to the discovery of benefits—including better sleep and reduced pain—from walking barefoot outside or sitting, working, or sleeping indoors connected to conductive systems that transfer the Earth's electrons from the ground into the body.

Furthermore, the soil itself contains mycobacterium vaccae which have a similar effect on neurons that drugs like Prozac provide. It can be said then that soil is a natural anti-depressant. It is no surprise to me because I am always happier with my hands in the dirt and maybe it also explains why mud-running has become so popular. All those smiling people covered in mud while doing a run for charity are quite probably on a natural high!

Kate's Garden

'The re-seen greenness' of spring was just one of the phrases in a long poem that Kate sent me describing what her garden in Hertfordshire means to her and her family. As Kate says she only gardens a little, her poem was further proof to me that just having a connection to a garden inspires and moves people and has real meaning in their lives. I was therefore keen to visit, hear more of what she had to say and see this personal paradise myself.

TWIGS in Swindon

Franzi the Head Gardener now and then

Amwell Cottage Hertfordshire

Iris and Allium at Woodlea Bottom

'Despair' sculpture at TWIGS

Jane's shed

Amwell Cottage is a lovely old place and before I've even come through the gate I love it, due largely to the old path edged with cobbles absolutely smothered in violets. Such a simple thing but so, so pretty. And as Kate shows me around the rest of the garden I am very impressed here by the lightness of touch. This isn't a show garden – it is subtle in its beauty so perfectly complementing the old house. It seems this could be the garden that the first owners and builders of the house might have made. I especially fall in love with the orchard with its daffodils and cow parsley among the long grass. It really does feel like we've stepped into the past.

In her own words Kate describes their garden:

A space for play when our children were small,
To dress up and hide in the trees, to play football,
find sticks, losing themselves,
A place to work the ground and muscles, to dig, to weed,
to swim, to swing
A lawn for reclining, a terrace for dining

Maybe the poetry disposes me to the notion but Kate's garden has a great sense of place; one of those things that I can feel but not define. It is something to do with the soul of a place and that soul being honoured by the garden and surroundings. It is easier to describe in the negative, in that it is somewhere where nothing jarrs. I would feel very comfortable living with this garden and working in it. The man that does work in it Kate now introduces to me. John, who helps them twice a week, used to work for ICI but left because he was desperate to get outside and he says he knows a lot of second career gardeners and designers who just had to get out of the office. I ask him if he had some sort of epiphany, hoping that he might have turned away from ICI garden chemicals and become an organic gardener. But he laughs and says no, it wasn't that so much as just needing to work outside. I joke that I am slightly disappointed by this lack of story, so as if to make it up to me he says that he's definitely seen a decline in hedgehogs over the last 30 years of gardening and I am partly remounted on my anti-chemical high horse.

I happily follow instructions from John to weed an area near the house, enjoying the sun on my face and the occasional chat with a fellow gardener, as well as the unexpected peace of the area. Later, Kate's husband Colin arrives home and joins us in the garden. Colin spends as much time as he can in the garden, when he's not working in London, and while he shows me his latest project outside, the County Organiser, Julie Wise and her husband Tim turn up. This makes me a little nervous as County Organisers sometimes can, but they turn out to be a very friendly couple and we all have a lovely supper together, chatting about gardening and plants and charities (Kate is involved with Hope & Homes for Children as well as the NGS) and the attachment we have to our gardens. Both couples rebuilt their homes from wrecks and say they would find it nearly impossible to leave having made their dream homes and gardens. I start feeling slightly nervous about my planned move from the garden we have made in Worcestershire, but if nothing else, this tour is teaching me that I can be happy in any garden – as long as I have a garden I will be fine. All will be well.

Kate, who is a teacher of children with special needs, may not have her fingers in the soil as much as some of us but her garden is obviously central to her life and she is very aware of its progress through the year. As she says in her poem:

The Wild Swan Anenomes or hostas mere thumbs in a pot
What hope have they got?
Such pot luck this gardening lark
Of sunshine and showers, fading daylight and frosts in the dark.
But at each rebounding Spring we all take heart
In the reseen greenness
In all the joy and glory of a garden

Stoke Poges Memorial Garden

It has been a bit of a revelation to me that places I thought of as being very built-up, busy, commercial and full of empty gardens belonging to commuters to London – places such as Surrey and Hertfordshire – actually have much more green than I expected. There is much said about our loss of natural habitats but there are still a lot of trees out there, even in the most populated areas, and of course gardens are one of the biggest sources of natural habitat for our wildlife in these areas. All is not yet lost.

Driving from the natural verges into villages and towns I see joyous celebrations of spring in the front gardens I pass and they make me smile. Collections of all that horticultural spring has to offer – blazingly multi-coloured patches of spring art cheerfully greet all that pass. Big blowsy pink cherry blossom and massive glossy magnolia flowers under-planted with the mixed blues of muscari, forget-me-nots and aubretia, in turn enlivened with all shades of tulips, primroses and daffodils. Surely even non-gardeners must notice, smile and be bedazzled.

My next visit is in another 'rich' county – Buckinghamshire and here in the 1930s the wealthy Sir Noel Mobbs, Lord of the Manor of Stoke Poges, acquired the twenty acres of land to the south St Giles' Church in order to preserve the tranquil and rural setting of the church, made famous by Gray's poem 'Elegy in a Country Churchyard' and to have the land as a Memorial Garden, to be a 'living memorial to the dead and of solace to the bereaved'.

Franzi Cheeseman is the Head Gardener at Stoke Poges Memorial Gardens. Franzi always knew she wanted to be a gardener – even when she was growing up in a Swiss city and had no garden. She tells me of her path from Switzerland to Buckinghamshire and I think how fabulous it would have been to go straight into gardening – to not have wasted so much time doing other, less fulfilling, things in my life!

The Memorial Gardens were designed by Edward White to be completely different to the dreary Victorian graveyards of the day. The Gardens were to contain no buildings, tombstones or monuments as in a cemetery, but were designed to be a peaceful country garden resting place.

"The idea was that it was to be a homecoming," Franzi tells me and the other interested visitors I have joined on one of the regular tours. The huge garden works as a whole with elegant wide paths, 30 fountains, an Italian water garden, an 80 year old wisteria and lots of yew hedges whose clippings are taken for cancer drugs each year. But within the overall design there are small gardens and family plots. Some of the plots are better maintained than others and Franzi tells me that they are not able to trace the owners of some. There were and continue to be in excess of 500 individual family gated gardens and while living family members take care of some of the plots, Franzi and her team try to keep on top of the rest but it can take a whole year to get round them all.

"When the garden was first made" Franzi tells us "there were 18 gardeners including a 'Garden Boy' whose job it was to keep the kettle going!"

Anyone can arrange a burial here and if the private spaces are a bit expensive, ashes can be interred or scattered in other areas such as the Oak Dell where an enormous 600-year-old oak has lived through the reigns of 29 kings and queens.

I ask whether Franzi thinks the ashes scattered or placed under turf here have helped the tree to have such a long life. Everyone laughs and I splutter that we gardeners often use mixtures of blood, fish and bone to enrich the soil in an attempt to show perhaps it wasn't such a silly question. Then I shut up, red-faced, while Franzi tells us that they actually blow nitrogen into the ground using a pneumatic drill-type-thing.

The Gardens are registered as Grade I Listed on the English Heritage Register of Parks and Gardens of Special Interest in England and are open all year round, dawn to dusk. Of all my visits this place touched me deeply, not least I suppose because for the last eight years I have been planning (in my head) a memorial garden for my lost baby daughter. I think of the solace making a little garden here must have brought so many people. Planting a garden in memorium to me is quite literally allowing the cycle of life to continue. I get a lot of comfort from thinking that the ashes of my daughter will help her memorial garden to grow. Someone once told me grief is love with nowhere to go. I think love needs a garden to go to.

Sara's Garden

The first of the RHS Flower Shows is in Cardiff and although it has been running for several years, this year is the first time I go and I love it. It is small compared to some of the other shows and that gives it a nice almost intimate party atmosphere. You can be sure to get around everything and see everything which I like because some of them are so huge you are never quite sure if you've missed the best bit or not.

I have arranged to meet Gill & Gordon Baston for a coffee while we're there. We talk about the bits we like and are not so sure about at the show. We like the folk walking about dressed as trees but we agree we're all too British to accept the invitation to hug them.

We all love the living wall in one of the show gardens. Like ours, though, Gill & Gordon's garden is nothing like a show garden. For them it's all about nature and started with a pond 20 years ago. Gordon is very interested in birds – especially falcons – and also is having great success in encouraging owls to nest in the shed he has specially built for them.

Gill tells me, "Our garden has many stories, the latest being Healing" and she explains that their daughter has been seriously ill and that the garden has helped them through this time by keeping their minds and bodies occupied.

Not far away in Dina Powys there is another 'healing garden'. Sara Bentley and her husband Trevor have created a garden from what was just a large expanse of lawn when they moved in. Using permaculture principles (permaculture is essentially the purest form of organic gardening), they set about turning this unusually large front garden into a lovely place to potter and sit. The first thing they did was to cover the existing lawn in cardboard and then heap piles of manure from the local stables over the top. They then left it for a year. This is a brilliant way of starting your garden with beautiful soil – if you can be patient enough to wait a year.

And Sara has plenty of patience, partly because she has been very ill and had to slow down entirely, retiring at only 36 because of a rare heart and lung condition. All Sara's gardening has to be done slowly. She cannot lift anything more than a small pot, cannot dig and cannot lift plants out of the soil. Fortunately this gives her time for good planning and having decided she wanted to make a garden and covered her lawn in muck, Sara attended a gardening course – and then another – and actually now can't remember which courses she's been on and what qualifications she's got, but says it is irrelevant because all she wants to do is make her own garden. However she does admit that "The more gardening folk

I met, the more I noticed they were often speaking Latin! So I wanted to do a course to learn Latin names!"

Trevor, Sara's husband, tells me Sara was so ill that the doctors told him at one point that she wouldn't come through the weekend. Sara remembers, with a laugh, that she was so weak when she finally came home that, having been settled into a chair in the garden by her family and surrounded with some pots and compost and plants that she could just enjoy gently potting up, she very slowly tipped sideways and fell to the ground without being able to stop herself.

Sara is adamant that gardening saved her life. "I had a great job as a social worker and I lost that – my whole life changed. Gardening and the dogs saved me! The garden gives me some kind of purpose – I'm achieving something and opening for the NGS really helps too because people come and ask you questions that you can answer. It's a real confidence-building thing."

"It's so absorbing – it's like my art – I get totally absorbed in what I'm doing. Being creative is so important."

I ask to see some of Sara's work and I love it – there is a beautiful picture of a dancer on the wall – a gorgeous hare (why is it always hares?) and some colourful seaside scenes in the pointillist style – lots and lots of tiny circles – I can see that painting them would have indeed been an almost spell-binding way to spend an afternoon and decide I would like to try it.

Sara and Trevor organise the village garden openings for the NGS and other causes in Dinas Powys as well as now running a B&B. They obviously love living here and say there are now very much part of the village scene "There's a kind of an informal mafia" they laugh "but there's a really good unit organising buses for the elderly, a music festival and of course the garden trails."

Despite her illness, Sara is obviously loving life and as she walks me around their garden, before I leave, it is clear she loves her plants too. She says, "I've been on the courses and I know I should be planting in drifts and all that, but I can't resist buying one of this and one of that – I just love plants!"

Kerrie & Pete's Garden

Such is my brilliant planning that having recently popped down to Buckinghamshire, then to Hertfordshire, then back for a quick trip to Wales, I'm now driving up to Hertfordshire again. Having sworn some time ago not to use motorways, I'm annoyed that my sat nav has tricked me onto the A1 which turns out to have M in brackets after it and is very motorway-like for a journey that was not supposed to have motorways. I get blown about like a feather and hang on with all my strength to the steering wheel trying to anticipate gusts from passing lorries and gaps in the hedges. I am quite exhausted from concentration and fear by the time I reach the home of Kerrie & Pete Lloyd-Dawson. They welcome me into their warm kitchen with the maddest collection of fridge magnets I've ever seen and I am immediately calmed by their friendly chat with coffee and biscuits.

I can see the garden from where I am sitting in the kitchen and I can see more of it in the albums of photographs they've laid over the large kitchen table to show me. I comment on the beautiful photography and am pleased that I've said the right thing when I learn that Pete is a professional photographer. Previously a journalist Pete suffered a breakdown which he believes came about because of his stifled creativity. When he was ill he wisely turned to the charity MIND and became a client. When they learned of his passion for photography they suggested that he went for walks

Tulips in Spalding woodland

Lunch at Deans Court

Nearly Amalfi

Kerrie and friend

NGS stand at RHS Cardiff

Three straws please

Kerrie and Pete's garden

with his camera and this is what he did. Taking photographs of nature and making the garden with Kerrie fulfilled his creative urge and helped his recovery. Now he actually leads Camera Walks for people referred to him by doctors. The Walks become a project with a focus on an exhibition at the end and this absorption in an artistic endeavour really helps other people in the same way it helped him.

I ask Pete's wife Kerrie if she is a creative sort too. She tells me she's a lawyer but that the garden is her expression of creativity. Pete chimes "Kerrie has an exceptional eye for form and colour and texture" and when they show me around the garden this is very apparent in the incredible array of those elements in the plants she's chosen. Foliage is really important to them. They want to enjoy a plant for all of its life not just when it is flowering. It's not a big garden – though their clever use of space makes it feel quite big enough – but they say they don't want to waste space on something that isn't going to give them pleasure for most of the year.

It is obvious that the two truly love their garden. Like me, they have no children and their nurturing instincts are played out on plants, hens and cats – we really are that alike! They also rescue plants through a fabulous charity called Waste Not Want Not which, like TWIGS back in Swindon, is a horticultural based social enterprise using horticulture as a therapeutic tool to assist in helping homeless people, ex-addicts, ex-offenders, the socially excluded, people with mental health issues and depression and those recovering from a life crisis. But another great aspect of this particular charity is that it seeks and gains donations from garden centres and places like B&Q as well as members of the public who give their unwanted plants which would otherwise end up in landfill. Waste Not Want Not nurture them and sell them at their nursery.

Pete and Kerrie particularly like the challenge of bringing on unusual plants and the excitement of something known as 'tricky' flowering for them, but also the everyday thrill of something new appearing in their incredibly well planted garden. There are some brilliant ideas in this garden such as the outdoor sitting room at the top of the garden with its chairs, fireplace and an old television serving as a nest box. This is done with great style and doesn't look like the junk yard I may have just made it sound like at all. Venturing further up a garden that I thought I had finished viewing is an amazing waterfall into a pool and not for the first time I think that people with small or 'normal-sized' gardens are so much more inventive and creative than those of us with acres. I would never have thought you could fit so much in to this patch of land and it doesn't feel squashed or cramped in the least. In fact it is so beautifully done that it reminds me of a show garden at one of the RHS Shows.

Kerrie, who I am fast realising is an amazing plantswoman, teaches me to love a smaller kind of dicentra (I've always had an unreasonable dislike of dicentra) and shows me alpines that will grow in shade. I fall in love with a raspberry coloured species tulip whose name I forget to write down.

The couple love sharing their garden with others for the National Gardens Scheme and I can imagine they've provided inspiration for many people in this busy well-populated area where land is a precious and rare thing. I certainly leave thinking how very unimaginative Willy and I have been in our garden. Kerrie writes a blog called A Garden Less Ordinary which precisely describes what their garden would do if it was in a tin.

Krysia's Garden

My last stop for now in Hertfordshire is at Pembroke Farm & Garden where I meet Krysia Selwyn-Gotha and her son Sam, who apart from anything else must be the heroes of the local wildlife having injected into a typical Hertfordshire 'arable desert' a mixed, healthy and resourceful habitat. Having moved out of London with images of living with the birds and other wildlife Krysia had been disappointed to find that there was not a single bird visiting her new garden. At a difficult time in her marriage, Krysia says the digging feeding and planting became addictive. "It was a haven of peace and yet creative optimism in my troubled world. The start was very slow, not least because I had to sequester saved money for my precious trees and shrubs. Every week I would buy what I could afford. Later I learned to layer and take cuttings to increase my stock."

"Finally in 2003 there was enough shelter to think about a grand plan for a county garden walk, coinciding with my interest in introducing pollinator and wildlife friendly plants. This was a particularly difficult time in my life; depression, fear and heavy burdens of responsibility were breaking my heart and spirit." Krysia tells me she hid in the garden when things were really bad, but that "One day I realised that he didn't underpin my life – the garden did and that made the break-up easier"

Krysia, has the most beautiful voice (I wonder if she's an actress and find out later she trained in drama but switched to art) and I happily listen to her speak about her belief in our innate connection with nature. "Today's world is one dominated by technology which suits and reflects the abilities and talents of a proportion of people. Sadly with the rise in this useful area of work and play it seems the aesthetic and sensitive capabilities have become marginalised into mere hobbies. For those of us whose talents and practical inclinations fall into the latter category, life has become a struggle to squeeze ourselves like round pegs into square holes, leading to unfulfilling lives, unable to realize our potential and by implication society is much poorer than previous centuries. When our antecedents look back at our time what artefacts will remain or be considered worth preserving? In terms of gardens it is even less likely as they are by their very nature – borrowed."

Sam, one of Krysia's sons, cheerfully bowls in and joins the conversation by telling me that he had found working in the city didn't suit him and says that in fact the city life depressed him. It became clear that, like his mother, he would not be happy unless he was gardening. "This, in itself seemed problematic" Krysia says, "because we considered ourselves hobby gardeners but having opened the garden for the NGS and loved it we felt perhaps we could open it more often and we could introduce some money making features which would enable Sam to carve his career here."

They make a fantastic team because Sam loves hedging and topiary and Krysia loves the more wild and flowery bits. Their garden to me feels like a delightful reversal of the norm: Where you might normally find a wild glade in a mostly formal garden, here you come across glades of grandeur by Sam set amongst the artistry of Krysia's wild-ness.

There is the most beautiful courtyard where lunches and teas are served next to huge pots of Sam's new passion – azaleas and rhododendrons and there is also a shop full of lovely gifts to take home.

Krysia says, "Gardening to me is indubitably a spiritual connection I need to make daily. Weeding in particular brings one so close one can learn a great deal about the personality of the individual plant. Like us no one is the same and through this I appreciate my own uniqueness and value."

"The thinking nature of all the tasks carried out in the garden so utterly absorb that little room remains for idle worries. Ultimately gardening illustrates the joys of life; optimism, renewal and of course the normalcy of the final sleep."

"Through gardening anyone can tap into their own creativity and heal their souls because nothing will ever again be as important as whether all the cyclamen come up in the spring!"

I couldn't agree more.

Lincolnshire is a bit like Venice in my mind (bear with me) because if you mention Venice people always say it smells and if you mention Lincolnshire, people always say it's flat. And it's as if that is it – no further comment is worthy. But Venice is a very beautiful, unique city with stunning architecture and art, and music and fine dining, and it's on water and it's got boats in the streets for goodness sake! There's quite a lot to say about Venice aside from the smell and I'm sure there is much more to say about Lincolnshire than the fact that it is flat as I drive towards it for the first time in my life.

However, the flatness is very real and keeping a firm hold of the Daisybus steering wheel is making my wrists ache as the wind veers me ever closer to slipping into a dyke. Nice long straight roads are edged either side with dykes made by the farmers of the 19th century to drain the land and make it workable, useful, rich, profitable. With fields either side of the dykes and no hedges or windbreaks for miles I'm thinking it must take some practice to get used to driving these roads. Certainly the locals are coming at me with no fear.

As I approach Spalding large signs suggest a visit to 'Springfields' but I'm not sure I want to spend time in a retail outlet this fine April day, so when I spot a smaller sign for The Bulb Museum at Birchgrove Garden Centre I decide to head there instead. The place is quiet when I arrive and I can't find the museum entrance but when I ask, a nice man says he'll get the key and open it up for me. I begin to wonder if the Bulb Museum is like our 'museum' at home – essentially an old barn full of stuff we've found in the garden (most of it not actually very interesting) – but when the key is turned and the door is opened I find myself in a small but very well presented series of rooms with life-size models of eighteenth century bulb growers and pickers with life-size models of horses pulling huge carts that would have been full of tulips and recreations of hovels with more life-size models of workers using the old tools, ploughs, bulb graders, weighing scales and sack winders. A video in the gardeners' theatre tells the story of this local industry from its conception through to its heyday and into its decline.

With all these models around and the clever paintings on the walls depicting stretching fields of colourful tulips, I really get the feel of how the area would have been in the days of 'Tulipmania' – a time when bulbs could fetch extraordinarily high prices and were traded on the London Stock Exchange. The realness is helped by the fact that the Museum is dedicated to all those who created and worked within the flower bulb industry from 1880 and many of them are pictured in the photographs on display.

2013 saw the last of the Tulip Parades that had originated from the 25-mile route the Tulip Growers' Association started in 1948. The tour went through the surrounding villages and country lanes as a huge-scale exhibition of the best fields of tulips. The tour was so popular that the police had to enforce a one-way system on the roads around the area. Nowadays, it is mostly daffodils that are grown here, as in the 1970s it became impossible for the farmers to compete with the growers in the Netherlands so I am not able to see this spectacle in reality. But, after leaving Birchgrove, I decide to take a look at Springfields after all as there is mention of 'Festival Gardens' there.

After parking up the Daisybus in a car park that must cover several acres, I walk through the busy parades of shops at Springfields, stop for a quick coffee and idly watch the ladies shopping and lunching before going off in search of the gardens. What I find takes my breath away and I cannot believe that apart from two other ladies I am the only one there to enjoy these huge displays of spring flowers and show gardens. What excites me most is finding a woodland area planted with tulips, which, I had always believed, need sun. But here they are in their thousands, looking incredibly beautiful in the dappled shade of the beech trees. With such a display I feel sure there must somewhere be a 'Bulging Bulb Shop' and look around for some indication of where that might be – a sign, an invitation, a gardener even? Nothing. No-one. I have an eerie feeling of the place being populated by the ghosts of the industry past – that only they place any importance on these April beauties; that they alone are standing admiring and rejoicing in this joyful spread of colour, knowing each flower by name and the price it will fetch at the now vanished market.

Determined to speak out loud my enjoyment of this display to someone other than the two ladies on the other side of the garden, I walk around to a working area where sheds and storerooms also appear to be mostly abandoned. But I find a girl, a gardener, to whom I gush my appreciation. She is rather taken aback and possibly doesn't understand me anyway, as she tells me in a what I'm guessing is a Polish accent that, "No we don't sell them" and "I think they come from Holland".

My heart fills with sorrowful love for these unnoticed beauties flowering madly away just yards from crowds of potential admirers. I walk back through the throngs of shoppers marching in and out of concrete shops and feel I need to tell everyone what they're missing. But maybe they saw it yesterday – or maybe they're going tomorrow – maybe they're planning a family picnic there for the weekend – maybe the tulips will still be loved.

Liz's Garden

Liz Dixon-Spain lives on the highest hill in Lincolnshire she tells me, when I arrive at The Old Vicarage at Holbeach Hurn not long after leaving Spalding. "We're 9 feet above sea level" she laughs, but she is sincerely glad that she has at least some form of shape to her land. Indeed, when in Liz's garden you really don't feel like you're in the typically level Lincolnshire landscape. Much of this is probably down to the fact that Liz is a garden designer and has made the most of what her predecessors kept back from farmland to make a garden.

Liz's garden doesn't look 'designed' and although I'm always nervous saying this to garden designers in case they take it that I am saying it's a mess, I do remark on the casual feel of the place. Liz says, "Maybe designers feel freer to be more loose and natural in their own gardens," and during the afternoon her attitude and style really encourage me to be less concerned with 'Doing Things Properly'. This is not to say that Liz doesn't know what she is doing, she is clearly a fine designer and plantswoman, but she works alone in this garden and there are many things that she simply cannot do herself such as drive poles for pergolas and fences deep into the ground. She gets them as far as she can and makes do and when they start leaning they look charming and rustic. They might get propped up or a plant might begin to camouflage the problem, but the result is that the garden has such character because of it. I wonder why I don't just get on and do these things myself instead of waiting for my husband to come out and 'do it properly'. A bit of fallen tree stuck into the ground and tied with string actually looks just as nice to me as a milled and treated square post set in concrete for eternity.

Liz is fun and has fun in her garden – she makes benches out of logs and branches, she makes experimental willow works – she just has an idea and tries it and enjoys the process. She says the garden fulfils her artistic needs, but the garden here has also been restorative for Liz. "It's absorbing," she says and so helps with the difficult and sad times in her life. She points to "Cancer Corner" that she made for her father. We speak about loss. "Grief becomes something you're familiar with and easier to bear because of that." She shows me another border that she dug over in frustration when one of her boys failed his finals. She laughs and tells me, "Friends say 'Oh dear, what's upset Liz? She's digging again!'"

We are followed around the garden by the soppiest spaniel who will not be ignored for a moment and who lies at my feet squirming and rolling when I try to leave – lovely eyes entreating me to stay for just one more scratch and cuddle – and I think it wouldn't be a hardship to stay in this lovely place – a little hillock of paradise in the land of forgotten tulips.

Wendy's Garden

The night before my visit to Wendy Cartrwright's garden in Dorset, I have my first experience of spending the night on a campsite in the Daisybus. I choose a site at Durdle Door and when offered a sea view I leap at the chance – who wouldn't want a sea view? Well, I guess people who don't want to park practically vertically on a cliff wouldn't. It's my first night camping and I am on a serious slope facing the sea. I notice that there are breeze blocks at each designated parking space and realise that I am meant to lodge them behind the wheels of the bus, which I do. But I am still nervous – What if the handbrake fails and she just rolls over the blocks? I leave her in gear – What if that fails too? I consider that I may actually have one of those moments in dreams where you are falling to your death – except this time waking up won't stop it.

Being early in the season there are not many people around but there is another VW camper – a more modern, cosier and better equipped version parked just along from me. I decide to ask for the reassurance I desperately need in order to get a wink of sleep tonight. Luckily I get it. A very nice couple who are obviously proficient campers smile benevolently at me and he says smiling, "You couldn't drive it over those blocks even you wanted to – she's not going anywhere. Just one would have done it." Despite feeling foolish that I have piled up six blocks behind the wheels, I feel I could kiss him.

I visit the site office to scrounge some hot water (did I mention I am completely unprepared for this trip –I have no heater, no stove and simply didn't think of obvious things I might need – like a towel if I'm going to use a shower block) Being a spontaneous, 'Free Spirit', actually doesn't suit the 50 year old me as much as it suited the 20 year old me I am discovering.

In the site office the two chaps there are friendly and helpful and give me my 'pass' (if that's what its called) and ask me to display it on the outside of my comfort screen. "My what?" I say, "Your screen that you put in your window" they say "Oh I don't have one of those" I say trying to sound like a hardened camper who doesn't need such soft mod cons. "What do you do when you want to get changed for bed then?" he says. "Oh… um….. I see ……" with embarrassed mutterings about making do with a blanket I shuffle off back to my freezing cold accommodation. I worry that I will run the battery down if I keep the light on long so sitting in pitch black, I decide on an early night. I barely sleep at all because I am sooo cold even with a woolly hat and pyjamas, a blanket wrapped around me and having rolled myself up in my huge kingsize duvet. I'm also disappointed to find that I am too long for the bed – my legs are crushed at the bottom of the bed against the cold back door. Much overnight grumbling. When I wake from an exhausted semi-sleep I realise that because I'm parked on the slope I had actually slipped down and been sleeping in the bottom half of the bed and that there was actually plenty of room above my head. However I am glad to be able to get on with the day and it is exciting to wake with a fabulous view of the sea I specially paid for and a beautiful day beginning. Driving along National Trust clifftop – the spring sea luminous blue below – I already know this is going to be a special place. I love gardens and I love the sea so for me this garden is perfect not least because it immediately reminds me of one of my favourite books The Enchanted April by Elizabeth von Arnim (also author of Elizabeth and Her German Garden and A Solitary Summer which are must reads for gardeners like me).

Arriving at Marren is like arriving on the Amalfi Coast. It is an enchanting place. I know I say that a lot but this is truly my idea of heaven.

Wendy welcomes me to Marren charmingly and I am unaware for a moment that they have been waiting for me to have lunch with them. I, on the other hand, had decided I would give them a chance to have lunch before I arrive, so I'm embarrassed that not only have I delayed their lunch I have just swallowed a garage sandwich and have no room to eat what has been prepared for me. Wendy and Peter are quite posh so I am doubly awkward about my faux pas but luckily being full rarely actually stops me eating so I enjoy a jacket potato looking out through the French windows from the kitchen to a living pergola made with hornbeam and the blue blue sky above the sea. It really does feel like I've arrived on the Amalfi Coast – I want to find a sunbed and sip a prosecco.

Despite being Quite Posh, Wendy is fun to be with, kind and totally real. She's a garden designer but apart from the area directly outside the doors to the garden which is more traditionally planted, much of the rest of the place appears almost wild. Of course it isn't really wild and an enormous amount of work and thought has gone into changing a bramble covered hillside above the sea into what is there today. Help comes in the form of a WRAGS (Work and Retrain as a Gardener Scheme) trainee – a banker turned garden and charity worker who loves the place. (An old school gardener turned down the job – it was a bit wild for him.) Wendy walks me around and up and down the garden and she doesn't need to tell me that it was a huge challenge making a garden on this sloping clifftop site. The worst part she says was moving stone for the paths and debris around to bonfire areas. "I wish I'd installed a pulley system before I did anything else!" she says.

Wendy links the more natural areas with bold designs of paths and steps – showing her intention and intervention whilst honouring the essence of the place. Losing myself in the natural beauty of the garden 'cake' I turn now and then and am reminded of the glorious 'icing' that is the view.

Again and again Wendy points out damage by deer and she also battles with rabbits, mice, rats, squirrels and bootlace fungus. Many trees have been lost. Some though, have been shaped by artist husband Peter who, with a chainsaw, has created subtle swirling columns that celebrate the life of the tree with a final flourish. But Wendy takes the knocks easily. She shows me a woven willow arbour she made years ago for the grandchildren. I say it doesn't actually look very old. "O no," she replies, "'I have to remake it every year because the deer eat it". Wendy doesn't seem to be unduly upset or uptight about the deer and when I sit on the benches and chairs scattered around the place and look out to the sea I feel that she must simply be way too happy to be frustrated by such small things. She shares Marren with wildlife – not in a hippy whimsical way like me – nor in a flatly matter of fact 'Them and Us' way. She's not happy about the deer and the fungus but she's not going to let it ruin or run her life either. These are just the cards she's been dealt with in the location she has chosen.

Peter has returned from collecting their dog who routinely disappears off to the local pub where he has become a regular (the dog not Peter). It's actually not very far from Marren as the crow flies and as the dog runs, but to collect him by car along the lanes takes much longer. I feel Peter has not had a very satisfactory day but he appears to have forgiven me for his delayed lunch by the time I come to leave and we chat about the Daisybus specs and the highs and lows of running a B&B business. I boldly ask them if they will be part of my next fund-raising project, Flowerbeds, which is to be a website of accommodation at NGS gardens and they like the idea which is thrilling. So I leave doubly happy about my visit to this fabulous place and I pull over on the clifftop path to ring Willy and drop a heavy hint that it would perhaps be a wonderful place to stay some time next year – perhaps in early April? (My birthday!)

Carol's Garden

The next day, after a similarly miserable night in the Daisybus, the day starts sunshiney again and my unheard whingeing soon stops as I enjoy the drive which takes me through happy-making woodlands of bluebells and wild garlic to my next destination – another of these very sweet Dorset villages, Ibberton where Carol Carsley lives. The idyllic cottage in this idyllic village is the happy ending of a story that ended in disaster for so many in the Second World War. Carol's parents were Jewish and escaped from Berlin to London in 1936. After the war they tenaciously applied for restitution money from the German Government having lost their livelihoods through Nazi racism. Carol's mother had wanted to go to university when she was young but Jews weren't allowed to go to university at that time so she got a job in the Post Office. She was later sacked from the Post Office for being a Jew and this was the basis of their claim for restitution because had she been allowed to stay in her job she would have undoubtedly been promoted with a better salary and ultimately received a pension. It was a long battle but eventually they were awarded the restitution and they decided to buy a cottage in the country so that their children and grandchildren might enjoy the sort of childhood holidays in the countryside that they had enjoyed in an earlier, happier Germany.

Carol inherited the cottage and she and her husband Clive also bought the house next door, so with the two properties they have a lovely large garden that they have both enjoyed making. After a coffee in her lovely cottagey kitchen Carol shows me through to an amazing garden room made mostly of glass, so that you really feel you are in the garden itself. With great hunks of oak providing the support it is quite the nicest room I've ever been in and in fact has won prizes for the architect and been featured in many a glossy home and garden magazine. The garden stretches gracefully in front of us away to the stream and the fields beyond but first my eye is drawn to a large border right by the house. "Wow!" I say. "That looks incredibly professionally planted!" and Carol is obviously pleased and says, "I try hard to make sure that border looks good because it's right next to this room so it is seen all the time."

The rest of the garden has a much less designed feel about it though and has a lovely stream running through with dwarf daffodils and primroses everywhere. The stream looks as though it's always been there but is actually the result of a lot of hard work redirecting and shaping. It looks and sounds quite lovely. As we walk, we talk and Carol tells me that she used to work in occupational therapy and how she knows that small, gentle tasks that absorb us are such a help for troubled minds and bodies. But Carol is obviously not one to live with her head constantly bent down to gardening tasks because, as we stroll, she regularly points out the views from the garden. The garden sits in the valley so much of the rest of the village is up around the outside edges of the garden. We're looking at what people call a quintessential English village and how marvellous it must be to have your garden set right in the middle of it.

I ask Carol if it is important to her that this cottage has stayed in the family and she says that there is a special sense of belonging. Carol's daughter Natasha Solomon was especially close to her grandfather and his story inspired her book Mr Rosenblum's List, which became a bestseller, with hopes for a film too. There will be no problem finding the perfect location for filming.

I happily work in Clive's vegetable garden and weed as much as I can in the time I'm here. Clive is away in London much of the time, having radiotherapy, and Carol says, "Coming back to the garden is a joy for him and he'll be so pleased that some weeding has been done!" Looking after the garden – their creation – in his absence is helping Carol through this worrying time too. I wish that I had more time to weed the whole raspberry cage to really make Clive's day but I have to go too soon.

Just before I leave, Carol's daughter, Natasha arrives with her husband and their son Luke. Luke is thrilled with the Daisybus and spends time trying each door and each seat and pretending to drive. I love him straight away for his VW enthusiasm and even more so when his parents tell me that he knows a lot of wildflower names already, including celandine; very impressive for two and a half.

I wonder if in time little Luke will become a student at nearby Kingston Maurward College which I visit the next day having been invited to attend their Silver Celebration marking 25 years of teaching horticulture. It's especially nice to be a part of this as my friend Tamsin is going to be there as she taught there for a time before becoming Editor of The English Garden magazine. Now she has moved on again and is running the totally amazing garden that has been in her family for years at Stockton Bury, very close to me in Herefordshire. We also run the Horticultural Hub together and we're very similar in that we're always having GREAT ideas – at least we think they're great ideas – though sadly none of them ever make us any money. But we are happy gardeners and money isn't everything......

It's fun to tag along with Tamsin, meeting all her old friends and having a tour of the gardens and teaching areas at Kingston Maurward while hearing their funny reminiscences from times spent there. Two trees are planted to commemorate the day – one for this 25th year's students and one for the past students and teachers that have returned today – photographs are taken that include me – who fits into neither category – but I nevertheless help to demolish the splendid array of cakes afterwards, so feel a part of the family.

Cake features a lot in garden visiting and my travels are making me choose from the larger end of my wardrobe as the spring turns to summer. I wonder whether the Daisybus is feeling the strain and as I get to know her better and feel fonder and fonder of her, I even start feeling that I should buy her something when I stop for a snack somewhere. Petrol doesn't really seem nurturing enough. These sorts of inconsequential thoughts drift through my mind on my long journeys. I develop a frustrating dilemma about what colour Fiat 500 I would choose. I am passing lots (well they're normally passing me actually) and they appear to have been produced in the loveliest of colours. I'm very impressed by Fiat's choices and can't decide if I would have the lovely pale blue, the perky pink or the beige (but perhaps beige is too beige – let's call it café creme) or what I can only describe as the Eau de Nil. Only a stylish Italian firm would choose Eau de Nil as a colour for a car I think – and then my idle mind says Eau de Nil is French and for another few miles I wonder what the Italian might be – but I get no further than aqua so decide to call it pistachio ice cream instead. Important stuff.

Deans Court

At least when my sunshiney flowery bus is parked up she gets plenty of attention from other people – lovely people like Kelly-Marie Burdekin who works at Deans Court in Wimborne. It's not surprising Kelly adored her because she is a very retro girl herself and carries off her vintage 50s look beautifully. Kelly runs the gorgeous café, helps in the vintage shop, helps run weddings and marketing and seems to be a wonderful all-round helper for Ali and William, the owners.

The organic walled kitchen garden at Deans Court produces food for the house and café as well as organic boxes for sale each week. Cut flowers that are sold in the shop and used for country-style weddings held in marquees on the lawn by the river, are also grown in the garden.

Ali and William brought Deans Court back to life having moved here from Gloucestershire. They always intended to make it a living, working place rather than a stately home museum. Their website is one of the most inviting I've seen. There are holiday cottages, spaces for family celebrations or weddings. Guests enjoy the sustainable lifestyle on the estate, including eggs from pampered chickens and honey from their bees, as well as the fresh, organic fruit, vegetables and salads all grown by Gardener Ellie, who coincidentally trained at Kingston Maurward College.

Ellie shows me around and tells me that she studied for a degree in conservation but changed to horticulture because she enjoyed the botany aspect of her course most. "I come from a family of gardeners and smallholders," she says. "I love growing veg – it's so rewarding". The sight of two polytunnels full of neat rows of young vegetables makes me envious – as does the light soil. "It's flinty but easily worked," Ellie tells me.

After my tour and friendly chats with the folk of Deans Court I enjoy the most beautiful salad I've ever had. Some might say it literally looks too good to eat, but it inevitably gets demolished pretty soon by me and again I return to the bus feeling bad I haven't brought a 'Daisy Bag'. I am so selfish.

Malcolm's Garden

In the bus I ring Malcom Orgee to see if it is convenient to visit the garden he wrote to me about saying, "I would say the reason of opening as part of the NGS was to let more people to come under the healing spell of this magical place". Although it's not possible for me to see the garden today, Malcolm tells me, "I have been involved with Puddledock for nearly four years now and originally came in as sub-contractor to carry out a few days planting and have been here ever since."

"I have worked most of my life in horticulture, starting at the age of three in my father's vegetable garden in Worcester. Since then I have been lucky enough to work in very varied gardens both in the UK and abroad. In fact I feel that Puddledock is a culmination of all of my gardening experience."

"We had only been living in Dorset for a few weeks before I was invited to develop Puddledock. When the owners, Ray and Ann, bought it seven years ago it was a boggy thicket of nettles, brambles and Goat Willow. This has now been transformed."

"Some of the structure of the garden was already in place when I arrived and a local nurseryman, Simon Goldsack, had planted a good number of shrubs and trees and some of the much needed drainage was already in place."

"What I am trying to achieve with the garden is a balance between what is an important habitat for Dorset wildlife and a garden full of interesting and unusual plants."

"When I said 'healing spell' I meant it quite literally. People who visit the garden become so absorbed by its atmosphere or by the detail of a single bloom, that it becomes a powerful therapy."

"The owners, visitors and those who work in the garden are all affected by its magic. I have friends who recently lost a child, they asked me if they could visit the garden and seemed to find some comfort there."

"Not long after starting work at Puddledock I was diagnosed with leukaemia and found that focusing on my work there has helped me come to terms with my medical condition. There are many more stories of people who find that the garden is a special place for them and feel compelled to return again and again."

Fiona's Garden

May – the best month of the year – the sun is up, the soil is warm and anything that is thinking of growing this year has started its path. The hawthorn is flowering in the hedges and the apple blossom in the orchards. All is well with the world, life is blooming and full of potential and I'm off to Essex. I have to admit that it is a struggle to leave the idyll of rural Worcestershire and head off to another county that in my imagination is a place of dormitory towns for London and somewhere high heels and fast cars are more common than my home turf of birdsong and tractors. But how perfect that I am heading for an island – near Colchester – and I imagine that I will be crossing a drawbridge away from the TOWIE crowd to an oasis of country calm. It's not quite like that when I arrive, but again I berate myself for thinking that the home counties have nothing to offer the nature lover as I drive down a tree-lined lane following signs to Green Island Gardens. What treasure I find! (It had to be said, didn't it?)

Fiona Edmond has made me supper and after she has shown me to my little chalet for the night we sit and eat in her huge kitchen with her many children popping in and out for seconds and puddings and she tells me her story – the story of the uncovering and making of this incredible garden and the recovery and possibly the making of Fiona herself…..

Following a stint on the amateur golf circuit and playing for England and Great Britain, Fiona decided the professional golf scene wasn't for her and returned to her first love of horticulture and plants.

"Gardening was my love and my business. I was a garden designer – designing for private clients in London," she tells me. "Was that very stressy?" I ask. "No", she laughs, I've been really lucky. I've never had any clients I wouldn't want to design for again – or if I have I've got out at the proposal stage! But it was the workload – I was trying to do too much. I'm the kind of person that if I take something on I won't be happy if I half do it – I want to do it properly so I kind of give 110% to everything."

But then after having two children and continuing her hectic London work life Fiona was struck down with the debilitating illness ME. "I was bedridden for six months and housebound for three years," she says.

Fiona is a dynamo – having been there only half an hour I can see that she is no slouch and just today is running a nursery, a garden, a tea room, six children and had two coachloads of visitors for lunch (she was only expecting one of them). It doesn't surprise me that even though she could barely sit up in bed she wasn't going to let ME beat her.

"I read everything I could get, especially about Dr David Smith who was successfully treating people, but only on the NHS and I wasn't in the right area so I couldn't see him," she explains. "So I read how he treated people and it was basically about forming a routine and making yourself do as much as you could every day, but not to the point where you overdo it – quite difficult to gauge!" "Even when I was bed bound I kept a strict diary, which he also advised, and every single day I marked out of 100 what percentage of a normal day's activity I had managed and the other thing was a score out of 10 as to how well I felt. Some days it was zero and I would honestly rather have been dead," she admits.

But Fiona remained hopeful and determined. "There were lots of 1s and 2s but then what the doctor told me was that if you plot that on a graph over time you see that you gradually go up up

Green Island Garden in Essex

Krysia's dog : "Just the cake please"

Alison's layered lawns in Lincolnshire

Westcote Farm, Lincolnshire

Green Island Tearoom

Kate Leese in her Sussex garden

up, and then you go down again. The frightening bit is that you can't stop the down bit once it starts – I knew I was getting worse every day but I couldn't stop that downward slide which was really frightening, really frustrating. The thing is they said just remember that the down won't be quite as far down and it won't last as long as the last time. And the next time when you go up – you go slightly further up and you probably stay up for slightly longer." This is the hope to which Fiona clung.

"It's so depressing when you improve and you think you're getting better and then you get hit again. I had a really bad relapse after three years – almost back to square one" she says, "but it didn't last anything like as long – I was only bed and housebound for a month rather than six months."

Her design work had to stop. "I had to completely clear my diary and have no commitments because I couldn't have the stress of not knowing how I was going to feel on that day – I didn't want to let anybody down. So I didn't make any commitments at all."

Fiona knew she had to leave London. They sold their house and with her husband and children she moved in with her parents for six months. Even though I was bed bound, I was lucky where we lived because my parents had a swimming pool – it was as much as I could do to get down the stairs or up in a day – that's how I started and then I made myself get into that swimming pool even if that was all I managed in one day. I wrote down how many widths or lengths I'd manage and I never went backwards. I always made myself do the same amount as the day before and then increased after a week and I started walking a little bit with the dogs and really slowly built it up."

"I was ill when we moved here. It wasn't really what we were looking for but we were getting desperate and my husband told me to ring up the agent and check we'd seen everything and he said you should really look at Green Island. We'd had the particulars already – it was a 1960s bungalow that needed work. I came over with my parents and I remember when we drove back nobody spoke for a while. It was something about the place it had a kind of spirit – a feeling when we came up the drive. I came back the next day with my husband and before we got to top of the drive this boyish grin came over his face and he said 'Let's buy it' – before he'd even looked inside!"

I'm by now engrossed in Fiona's story which begins to sound like a fairytale (apart from the ME bit obviously).

"It was terribly overgrown with fallen trees everywhere. The previous owners lived here almost in total isolation – nobody was allowed in or out, not even the milkman. When we moved in the postman knocked at the door and asked what we'd like him to do with our mail. I said 'Put it in the letter box?' and he said 'It's just that we've never been allowed up here before.' There was a lot of secrecy surrounding the place. There had been a garden – a couple of shrub beds and a kitchen garden that had been grassed over. There was a pond which we didn't discover for 18 months until the dog went in a thicket and came out stinking. It wasn't till we moved here that I discovered what was here. I would go out each day with the Labrador in the morning, even though mornings were bad for me. I'd go out for my five or ten minute walk and I'd come back in and say you'll never guess what I found today and it was another shed – but all these sheds had running water, electric, they had beds in them!"

"As a garden designer, the first thing I did was I got a land surveyor in and then the next was a rabbit fence. I was very lucky because my father is a farmer so he has the diggers. I was poorly but I was able to sit at my drawing board to design. The idea was to make enough garden just for our family and for me to display my favourite plants. I brought a lot of plants with us from London in pots and I dug a few cuttings and bits and bobs from my Mum's garden and just a bit of lawn for the kids and the dog really. The minute that I mentioned to my father that I had something on paper, that was it – he was here with his JCB and my brother came with the chainsaw and it all started happening – even though I wasn't really ready for it. My parents found my illness hard to accept and I know my father felt helpless and desperate to help in any way he could. I think he thought that if he got me out there doing the garden that was going to make me better. I never saw it like that but what it gave me was that every morning when I woke up instead of focussing on how ill I felt, it was the garden – what are we doing today? Even now if I ring him he'll drop everything to come and help. That's been his way of supporting me."

It's time for the children to go to bed and I trot over the gravel to my cosy wooden chalet. The next morning everyone is occupied with their jobs and I take the opportunity to look around on my own.

The garden is huge but has a very personal feel, I think because there is no great country pile sitting in it – there is just a rather modest looking family house which in no way competes with the natural surroundings. The woodland is full of curious follies and artworks made for or by the children or in memory of a previous nanny or friend and bluebells, bluebells everywhere – I make a note in my book that Green Island Gardens is a wonderful place if you're a bluebell lover, or indeed a bluebell, and I have a curious desire to become Mrs Pepperpot (who I hadn't thought of in years) and walk among them looking up into their bells. With the sound of the busy Essex roads in the background the birds seem to be rejoicing in song at their luck of finding this island haven and it occurs to me again that spaces like this are all the more important in busy areas, although from the garden all you can see outside is fields.

Meeting up again with Fiona she tells me what's going on today and I marvel at how much she has taken on. It is becoming quite clear to me that she is the sort of person who doesn't like wasting time, even when she was ill. She tells me, "I thought, I'm not sitting here wasting my thirties – if I can't do anything else I'll produce children! We had the mindset that we were paying a nanny anyway so if she was looking after two she might as well look after three. It felt like I was achieving something, which helped. We were lucky that we had the chalets in the garden we'd discovered so we were able to offer a home for nannies and boyfriends or husbands. So they had a home here too. We had two very special nannies. Annie the Nanny who basically brought Sam up as her own baby and then we had another one, Lisa, who was with us for three years and then when the youngest got to two, I decided we didn't need nannies any more and we could have au pairs and then it worked really well because I had help with the children and help in the garden."

Green Island Gardens just grew and grew...... Fiona continues as she shows me around the nursery, where I get the impression that the plants are some of the happiest I've ever seen. "It made sense to produce the plants for clients so the nursery grew from that and also visitors to the garden can buy the plants they see in the garden." Lush ferns and epimediums catch my eye and I start a mental shopping list that will become real before I leave.

While preparing lunchtime food for visitors, Fiona tells me, "Having discovered I could take on an apprentice with the help of the government scheme I interviewed a lovely lad who had been working in McDonalds but didn't want to do that, he wanted to work outside. I offered him the position but he said he'd been offered a two-week placement with a landscaping company so he couldn't give me an answer straight away and asked me if I'd mind waiting two weeks? I was impressed that he was looking at his options and agreed. But then I got an email from 36-year-old girl who'd been an engineer in the army working in Afghanistan fixing Apache helicopters. She was looking for a complete change of career. I thought this girl's got guts and I hadn't got the lad, so I interviewed her and was so impressed I offered her the position. The very next week the lad, Dom, came back and said he'd like to come and do the apprenticeship. Actually I thought we were at a real watershed point here with the business and it's not going to cost me any more time to teach two as one so we took them both on. Dom does the chainsaw and heavy stuff, although actually Amy is quite capable herself. Her big interest though is doing the marketing."

It seems to me this is one big, happy, extended family and I ask if Fiona's children are showing an interest in being involved in the garden too. "The children are more interested in the tearoom than the garden – my daughter especially – she's a real entrepreneur! People do spend more on tea and cake than they do on plants! I don't understand it."

We talk more about the healing power of the garden and being absorbed in gardening tasks and Fiona tells me she is not the only one who has found the place restorative.

"Yesterday a lady with advanced dementia and her son came. He emailed afterwards and said they'd had such a lovely time, they'd bought a season ticket so they can come back any time. He's a full-time carer and also cares for others with dementia and he asked if he could bring his mother back for a TV programme about dementia and interview her in the garden."

It certainly is a peaceful and tranquil garden. I work with Amy for a couple of hours in a huge border near the house and I notice that the plants in the borders are given plenty of space to be themselves. It's something I need to learn to do – our garden is overcrowded and I am realising that this comes from not knowing our plants well before we started. Fiona knows her plants well and she makes sure they have what they need to fully be themselves. There is a lovely feeling of things being able to breathe – you can almost hear them sighing in pleasure.

While we work Amy tells me that she too had been ill – suffering from stress and anxiety during her time in the army, leading to her leaving on medical grounds. "I couldn't improve things for my team," she tells me, "and I became very depressed, distressed and anxious because of it."

Amy is so much happier now. "I knew I had to totally change my life," she says, "but I think parts of my old job very much marry up with this job. I was very particular about ways things are done and that is good here too."

Over lunch with Amy, Dom and Fiona they all agree the place has special meaning in their lives. Dom says he wanted to garden from very young but got obsessed with his girlfriend's parents garden last summer. He did his A levels but he wanted hands-on work. He tells me he enjoys the peace and creative opportunities and he says he takes great pride in his work here.

He and Amy are both encouraged to be creative in the garden and come up with new ideas and they all talk of the peace here even when there are lots of visitors. There is enough space for everyone to have their own moments of privacy. Fiona says, "We all three love it when it's just us out there in the winter, but I start getting tetchy because there's no money coming in!"

With another coachload of visitors due this afternoon, I think it is time to leave this happy team to do what they do best and take my little yellow bus back onto the Essex roads. As I leave with inadequate words of praise for the place, Fiona tells me, "This is where I was always meant to be. I am philosophical – I think things happen for a reason and I think I got ME as a kick up the backside to get out of London. I was like a caged animal in London. I was meant to be a free spirit outside. I feel like this is where I belong."

Kate, Kit & Ceri's Garden

Not far away, a much smaller Essex garden in the village of Bradfield has had just as much healing power as Green Island. Ceri and Kit Leese contacted me to tell me their story.

"Just over three years ago our beautiful talented daughter set off for school in her first teaching year. That day our lives changed – Kate had an accident. She sustained multiple injuries, including a severe brain injury and was in a coma for nearly six weeks. During those weeks in early July we visited Kate in hospital and came home to the garden. It was such a comfort – I deadheaded the petunias and gazed at the bright colours of the begonias in the conservatory," says Ceri, "and Kit drew the delicate white flowers of the delphiniums whilst we were spending hours in the waiting room."

Kate miraculously survived and as we all sit around their kitchen table with a choice of delicious looking homemade cakes, she tells me how she had always enjoyed gardening herself and that when she was at university in Durham she started a students' garden in the quad. It was a shared garden though she ended up doing most of the work – and was perfectly happy to do so – and she still enjoys helping in the garden here at Chippins. When Kate first came home after six months in hospitals and care units, she was in a wheelchair, but now walks and overcomes new challenges every day. It is a part of her brain that controls 'executive function' that has been affected, so Kate's natural intelligence is still there, but is frustrated easily" her father, Kit, tells me. "There aren't many places Kate can relax but the garden is somewhere she can just be – it has a calming effect on her."

And I can see as her parents walk me around their garden that Kate isn't the only one who benefits from time spent there. "A little nurturing of the plants in your garden nourishes you – it helps you back into the world," says Ceri, "the beauty remains the same whether you are devastated or in the pink – there is that constancy. I don't know where we would be without our garden through all of this. It nurtures and feeds all of us."

Sarah's Garden

I had many invitations to gardens that 'have been in the family for generations' which, whilst I knew were interesting in a historical sense, initially I felt weren't quite the sort of story I was looking for this time. Indeed many books have been written about great gardens and their history. But I was after stories of how gardens have affected people's lives in a more profound way, I thought, not country piles that have had a succession of wealthy owners and gardeners who felt they had a duty to continue what their forebears had started.

But through visiting other gardens I came to see that history and family do of course, in themselves, affect people. There is an understandable pride and sense of achievement people feel at managing to maintain a beautiful and historic place – places that are sometimes considered of national importance. And the owners of these places are very often managing with far less than their antecedents in the way of skill, labour and finances. It must often be the case that they would in fact rather throw in the towel and sell the place to a chain of hotels, but pride, respect and admiration for their mothers and fathers and grandmothers, great grandfathers and so forth drive these present-day owners to find ways to honour the past and keep a garden alive and relevant to the present.

And there are of course perhaps new gardening dynasties being nurtured now. I think this when I meet thoroughly modern families such as the Murches at Ellicar Gardens. Sarah Murch is a truly Olympian gardener to my mind. I'm in Yorkshire in mid-May when most people's gardens are looking lovely but when Sarah and William Murch's is quite frankly breath-taking. OK, Sarah is a garden designer so it should be good but what I particularly love here is that garden, family and animals mix in together so happily. The piece de resistance that has featured in many gardening glossies is the natural swimming pond which is used daily by the family in the warmer months and acts as a bright shining example of the sort of thing Sarah and William can produce for clients, being, as they are, one of the foremost natural swimming pond makers in the country. With 'beaches' and pontoons and gentle planting around the water it is the most enviable pool I've seen and when I win the lottery I will definitely be asking Sarah and William to make one for me....

But this is just a part of what makes this place so special. To me the garden actually feels like part of the family. The dogs run through the borders as we walk around and Sarah is relaxed about it. She takes the view that you've got to live in a garden and not worry about a little flattening by children and animals now and again. And in any event, she chooses her plants well so that most of them can withstand even her daughter riding her pony around the garden and jumping over the flowerbeds. I totally love that feeling of freedom here. Behind the natural pond other animals are clearly visible, looking over to see what is going on in the garden (we've driven the Daisybus in to get a good pic). The most gorgeous goats with long glossy golden coats steal my heart and are yet another thing to go on my list of desires. Willy and I have supper with the family in the kitchen and it is not until half way through the meal that I notice a baby crow swaddled in a blanket on the work top. Another addition to the family that they are all helping to survive, having fallen from his nest and been abandoned. He landed in the right place here.

Sarah, who looks way too young to have achieved so much already, tells me that in Austria where they lived for ten years, "We started gardening to make somewhere for the children to play. We had a small garden with a Shetland pony for Izzy, two apple trees we used as goalposts and a trampoline with plants around it – it was all designed around the children and pets really." When she was pregnant with their son George, Sarah did a garden design course and now, as well as creating this garden and designing and making gardens and swimming ponds for clients, running their small nursery and caring for children and animals, Sarah is involved with school and community gardening groups and has weekly sessions with schoolchildren in her own garden.

She started by designing George's primary school garden and Sarah says children are naturally drawn to gardening "We are a generation of non-gardeners, but the children at schools now are so quick to pick it up. If the teachers gave ownership of the gardens to the children it would work even better but sadly they often don't allow them ownership and so the children don't get to go in at the right time to do the right jobs – so they can sometimes fail."

Sarah thinks children sit inside too much. "It is possible to teach everything outside – science, maths – everything could be done outside but they keep them inside and it's difficult for children to sit down all day indoors." As she speaks I recall being taken for lessons on summer days under the big horse chestnut tree at my primary school. I remember it as one of the very few times I liked being at school.

"The local primary school comes down here now for gardening classes. It's actually an absolute joy working with those kids." And she tells me of one little boy with a difficult background. "His face – his whole being – lights up when he is here. He made me that nest box," Sarah says pointing to a box full of chicks in her aviary. "But sometimes the children just dig up stones and wash them – it's just about being outside."

Sarah is obviously someone who has difficulty saying no (maybe she doesn't even want to say no) She is involved in so many projects that I feel exhausted on her behalf. But she clearly has a lot of her energy and on top of everything else I discover she's part of the local Britain in Bloom judging panel, which surprises me as I had always had an image of such panels being made of rather officious humourless councillors, something Sarah is emphatically not. I'm pleased when she tells me, "It really brings communities together. When you come to see a new garden you find that probably the following year the next door's garden is much nicer and it goes on down the street and you find that people are talking to each other – it really changes the atmosphere – makes a massive difference," she says, "and they're always immaculate – not like ours!"

Sarah got her green fingers from her mother, Helen, who also has a fabulous garden (designed by Sarah) open for the NGS. Handily for us, Helen runs a very nice little B&B not far from Sarah's garden and Willy and I have a very happy stay there for two nights and I make a note to ask her to join my Flowerbeds project too. This is exactly my sort of B&B – somewhere you are very welcome and cossetted, a beautiful garden to wander around and a nice pub over the road. Helen looks after us in a kindly, motherly way spiced up with her wicked humour which surprises us and makes us giggle with her.

Helen has arranged for us to visit some other gardens in the area while we are there and after breakfast we walk around to see

Jeanine Towler at Honeysuckle Cottage. This is one of those classic 'small but perfectly formed' gardens. In the top garden, a beautiful old herringbone brick wall with a cobbled path running along the bottom and an ancient fruit tree ooze history and Jeanine says, "There is a definite atmosphere here that is different from the rest of the garden" and tells me of the tranquillity she feels when gardening. It is obvious to me that she spends a lot of time 'tranquilly gardening' because it is sooo neat with some lovely features like the rusty cages for peas to clamber over, a tiny cornus I've not seen before, some amazing burgundy seedheads on a hellebore and a couple of toy animals hidden among the pots that amuse visiting children. The little china donkey fell out of a wall that was being rebuilt. Jeanine threw it under a hedge, but it kept turning up again and again in the garden, so now it lives in a pot by the door – a stubborn, persistent donkey that was not going to be ignored. I have one just like it at home.

Helen has also arranged for us to meet Sheila Clark at Holmes Villa who also has more than one or two small, quirky additions to her garden– in fact the garden is stuffed full of them. When we arrive and are shown the first bit of garden near the house I wonder if actually it's going to be a small gnome garden full of bits of junk that is going to disappoint, but I am so wrong. The tour gets better and better as Sheila shows us around her beloved garden – she's a plantswoman with a real flair for creative planting and display. I'm particularly struck by the many varieties of lovely ivies smothering banks and climbing old trees and fences, the small trees and the collections of bits and bobs; tools, baskets, scarecrows stacked and displayed here and there – some in lovely old wooden bus shelters thrown out by the council. The hosta garden is lush, the lake is surrounded by oxe-eye daisies and full of happy teal and ducks, and just about everywhere you turn something makes you smile.

Alison B's Garden

Leaving the family and friends of Sarah Murch in Yorkshire we head back into Lincolnshire but this feeling of kinfolk being pulled together and enhanced through their connection with the natural world is reinforced when we visit Alison Baugh in Lincolnshire. Alison says that their garden was especially designed as a place for their children from previous marriages to play and bond. It was important to them to get the garden right before the house; "The garden came first to make it safe and child friendly," Alison tells me as she shows me around. From a slide covered in fairy liquid to camp fires, wet suits in the pond with little boats, a cleverly concealed football pitch and trampoline area (hidden by yew hedging), Alison's reminiscences of times spent in this garden bring the place alive for me. Now the most important aspect of the garden is the huge quantity of luxurious garden furniture. "With five children all growing up and socialising we need a lot of room for youngsters to lounge!"

Alison's enjoyment of gardening started with her grandfather who loved to grow vegetables. "He knew the Latin names and entered vegetable and flower shows," she tells me. "I remember the smell of the greenhouse and the tomatoes and helping to carefully load exhibits into the back of his Morris Traveller and sitting in the back holding his standard fushias upright on the way to shows. After the show he'd sell the veg from the back of the Traveller. He wasn't interested once they'd won or lost," she laughs. "We used to enter the Vegetable Animals class or the Miniature Gardens classes that they had for the children using margarine tubs for ponds -

I remember the excitement of going back into the tent when the judges had finished to see what we'd won."

Until recently it was Alison's husband Gary who was the main gardener but now his time is taken up training for an Iron Man Challenge in Austria later in the year. When we visit, he's off training on his bike, but when he returns briefly it is clear he is still a gardener at heart when his phone rings and he starts negotiating for some Chelsea tickets.

Son Cam now does the mowing. Alison tells me it wasn't a smooth transition. "The mower beeps when the basket is full and Cam didn't know that Gary had been tipping the grass from the basket over the fence for the neighbouring cattle. So the first time Cam did the mowing, at the sound of the beep, the cows came running, broke down the fence and came running through the garden to get to the cuttings." Poor Cam – he's stuck with it though.

We are hearing such stories while having tea in next door's shed, which is not a 'shed', but a very fine 'pavilion'. We've been taken next door to meet Ian and Lesley who also open their garden for the NGS and are enjoying the humorous rivalry between the two couples. Gary and Alison call the pavilion the shed because Lesley and Ian call their 'summerhouse' the 'postbox' because it is so much smaller. The place is full of laughter as we tuck into tea and cake and I can see that for these people a little friendly one-upmanship and teasing makes gardening all the more fun round here.

I discover that Ian and Lesley both worked in horticultural therapy for years helping mental health patients get back into work. Ian finds clipping hedges very therapeutic himself, and he also enjoys using an Allen scythe in his new orchard, rather than mowing. He tells me he's aiming for the old orchard look of fresh grass growing up through the old scythed grass underneath the fruit trees he has carefully chosen. "An orchard should be half product, half beauty," he says.

The converted farm buildings connected to these gardens are some of the most beautiful I have seen with the traditional local 'tumbling-in' of the brickwork. That, and the laughter ringing through the gardens, would make it a very tempting place to relocate I think as we reluctantly take our leave at the end of the day.

I'm particularly interested in the link between art and gardening and the perennial question: Is gardening an art form? I like to believe it is, though I think of myself as more like a painter of scenery in a theatre than a painter of pictures for the wall. My garden art is the scenery to my life story. So I was delighted to hear 'proper' artists of all kinds telling me about the importance of their gardens to their art.

Yvonne Sonsino wrote to me inviting me to her garden near Newbury in Berkshire. She wrote: "Many years ago I took a flower-arranging class at night school. I was a young mum in my twenties at the time and had always had a fascination with plants that went beyond casual. I was intrigued by the way plants grew, with the lines and forms and movement they make, and with colour and fragrance. I was hooked from the first lesson, and pushing the pram for walks out with a new baby I had one eye on the little feet and arm movements in the pram and the other on the swishes and lines in the hedgerows and gardens that I walked past. Plants became a deep-rooted fascination (no excuses for the pun).

The shape of a lupin floret, the burst of a poppy, the scent of old roses, the freshness of mint, the soft flow and rustle of grass as it moved under the shade of a slim silver birch tree are memories from my early childhood that are with me now as strong as ever. How to put plants together artistically and blend colour and form were learned through many more flower-arranging classes and competitions. These learnings have influenced my gardening style which now influences my painting style. Composition and colour are crucial elements to gardeners and artists and I hope to capture harmony in both pleasures. Botanical art is my current area of study, and it enables me to delve deep into the details and perfection of nature. I couldn't ask for more than to have found such wonderful ways to relax."

And Yvonne, whose husband is also an artist, says gardening ticks a lot of boxes for her "It's a source of exercise, peace, artistic expression, scent, colour, family experiences, sounds and wildlife. In fact we love it so much we bought a 10-acre woodland in Devon as our 'overflow' space last year. This is when gardening becomes an extreme sport!"

Back in Yorkshire again due to more inept planning, I'm looking forward to meeting another artistic gardener after our stay at Monk Fryston Hall for a proxy trip down memory lane. My parents had their wedding reception at this historic hotel in the Vale of York so when I found it was perfectly placed for my trip I was keen to go and have a look. I invite Willy along for the Yorkshire trip as it's a long way to go in a Daisybus and I want the backup. Willy once drove to Pakistan in a campervan with four friends in the 70s – four boys and a girl on a mad hippy tour. They had lots of adventures that I have heard about often, but above all my overriding feeling about their trip is always one of pity for the girl. I don't like sharing the bus with Willy let alone three other men. In fact, one of the good things about inviting Willy on some of my trips is that we get to stay in hotels because we know our marriage would never last more than a few hours camping in the bus.

We took Mum and Dad's wedding album with us to Monk Fryston. It's still a popular wedding venue and the current owners are interested in tracing the history of the garden so were excited to see evidence of some old borders in the photographs. While we are there we take some new photographs too – one in particular is very important: we promised my father that we would recreate the most famous of their wedding photographs, in which he appears to be wearing a strange and enormous hat, which is actually the fountain behind him. He still swears the photographer was stitching him up. Willy dutifully stands in front of the fountain while I snap away, giggling.

Alison P's Garden

I'm looking forward to finding more evidence of art and gardening in unison as I travel to meet Alison Pollock. Alison has used her artistic experience in the making of her garden in Aldwark, Yorkshire. Incredibly, she has a high-flying city job in London but her dream home is here in her home county. How does she manage that, I wonder, as I drive around her Yorkshire village trying to locate her garden. That is one big commute.

All becomes clear when I meet the dynamic 'Nutmaiden' from Twitter. Tall, beautiful, extroverted and full of smiles and laughter I soon believe Alison can do pretty much anything she sets her mind to. Not least of her achievements is her exquisite garden, which immediately seems to me to be like one of those cute, stylised drawings of a perfect garden plan. And she's done it all herself. Having convinced him to move back to her roots in Yorkshire, becoming a gardener is something her husband steadfastly refuses to do, but this is not a problem for Alison as it is very much Her garden and has been transformed from a small paddock through her own hard work led by her gifted artistic eyes.

Alison tells me her father bred plants "He didn't have a garden though – more of a collection of plants." She and her sister used to help him cross pollinate daffodils with paintbrushes when they were little, so she started proper gardening young and she really knows her plants. Having lived in London and grown her career in finance, Alison was keen to return to her roots and make the garden her father never had and being obviously super-capable, she has been able to continue working for the same firm but work most of the time from Aldwark. She's even installed electric sockets in the sun trap gravel garden at the back of the house so that she can work on her laptop outside in the summer.

Alison shows us around the garden, occasionally darting off to take a business call, and we marvel at the perfection before us. But this is not a place where opportunists are not welcome: self-seeding softens the edges – so long as they're the right colour. Alison is very driven by colour and doesn't like clashes. She tells me she has a photographic memory for colour and her experience of mixing paints and knowledge of pigments makes it easy for her to know what will look good with what. I am impressed but Alison is critical of her ability "I don't have the original innovative ideas of a real artist, but I am able to recognise a good idea and I think I'm good at implementing them," she says.

Implementing them has obviously been a joy for Alison and also a healthy escape from her stressful job. It's clear her garden is her reward for the 200 mile virtual, and often real, commute to her work and spending time there is certainly having a big effect on me as I realise for the first time that there is a different kind of peace that comes from perfection. Am I feeling more peace here than from our 'natural wild garden'? Does order bring calm to the mind? Beauty abounds here – it is not sterile or uniform and certainly not boring – but this well-planned garden is in no way a rampaging jumble like mine. It has a feeling of human idyll

– woman-made idyll. Sometimes nature can just be a little too chaotic perhaps. Maybe when we make a garden, we're putting nature in order and creating calm in our crazy world. Maybe I need a more orderly garden for a healthier mind? But the thought of the battle ahead to create order out of the chaos that we have only just finished creating could lead to madness so I decide on the easier option of visiting tidier gardens than mine in the National Gardens Scheme when I feel the need of a calming dose of orderliness. My grandfather would have liked orderliness I think and I toast him and my grandmother this evening when I visit my grandfather's old local The White Horse at Ledston – where he only ever ordered a half pint. He might have more than one, but it was always 'only a half'.

Rosie's Garden

No-one is more aware of the many health benefits of gardening than GP Rosie Hamlin. Struck down by illness two years ago, Rosie suffers heart palpitations and extreme fatigue as well as dizziness which mean she has been unable to drive. Thus her life has become almost entirely focussed on her home and garden in Doncaster. After years of caring for others, Rosie has been forced now to look after herself. Luckily she already had a beautiful garden so the back breaking work of starting a garden had been long finished. On some days though even gentle maintenance would be too much for her and she still finds that sometimes, because it feels so good at the time, she stays out too long "On a good day of course I do far too much and then I feel awful and have dreadful palpitations. As long as I don't overdo it though, I feel better for a spot of gardening."

"As a GP and a gardener I'm very aware of the health benefits – reducing stress, being in the sunshine and just achieving something. So yes I try. It's just sometimes it's a bit of a vicious circle – if I do too much I suffer. But I always have better sleep after being in the fresh air."

I ask Rosie if as a GP she would prescribe gardening as a cure for people, as has been recommended in a recent report. Rosie says, "I think you have to motivate people, because you can encourage exercise but if people don't want to do it…." "You have to target it to the right people and I think one of the difficulties is having an access point."

Over lunch with Yorkshire County Publicity Officer for the NGS, Jane Cooper, we talk about access to green spaces in cities and Jane tells me about a project in Sheffield where housing estates and derelict land have been planted up by a group headed by Nigel Dunnett (one of my Horticultural Heroes) from Sheffield University to create a new open community area. "Everything they did got trashed and vandalised at first, but over the years, as they have involved all the local people and schools, so all the kids from nursery onwards have become involved in the place and the vandalism has stopped. Because they're growing up with it they care, because it is their garden."

This initial project has now grown into a social enterprise called Green Estates. To me it is one of the most inspiring and encouraging stories of public interconnection with their own land. Jane says, "There's an area where anybody local can take over a plot. There's a man from Eastern Europe who wanted to grow food that he would grow at home and finds difficult to buy in this country," she tells me, "he's growing all specialist Eastern European vegetables and he's now made a business out of it, selling fresh herbs to restaurants in London because they can't get hold of it anywhere else."

The Green Estates project grows and grows, involving all sorts of people and all sorts of unlikely places, encouraging people to connect with their environment in a meaningful way. If I lived in Sheffield I would be hugely keen to become involved.

Janet's Garden

Leaving Yorkshire to head back home to Worcestershire we travel via Leicestershire and unusually for this trip our destination is a large town – Loughborough – where Janet Currie and Pete Mosley live. Janet tempted me into the smoke and traffic I've been trying to avoid by telling me of the Secret Craft Fair, which she holds in their small suburban garden that they also open for the NGS.

Janet is very involved with the arts as a freelance consultant & project manager working with creative people and organisations. She has also set up her own project 'The Refectory Table' – providing events and courses that help people grow in confidence and creativity in business, as well as personally. Pete is a business coach and has recently published a book called The Art of Shouting Quietly. I'm relieved to hear that it's not one of those horrid, self-help assertiveness books that appear to sanction people being downright rude and insensitive, but more a way of teaching calm confidence and belief in yourself.

Whilst both of them work in the garden Janet leads on the design and planting. "I garden as a way to gather my thoughts – or let them just wander. I take a fairly painterly approach to planting. Gardening is another aspect of creativity and I enjoy the peace and connection with nature, but also I would describe gardening as an optimistic activity – there's also a different quality of peacefulness."

OPEN GARDENS & SECRET CRAFT FAIR
LOUGHBOROUGH

ngs
gardens open for charity

Festival
Weekend
7- 8 June 2014

COME AND VISIT:
LOVELY GARDENS, ARTS & CRAFTS,
TEA, CAKE & PLANT SALES

SAT & SUN: FAERIES AT THE
BOTTOM OF THE GARDEN
SUN: POTTER'S WHEELS,
IN THE SHED

FOR MORE INFO
WWW.THESECATEUR.COM
TWITTER @CRUMBHUDDLE

CHARITIES SUPPORTED INCLUDE MACMILLAN CANCER SUPPORT,
MARIE CURIE CARERS TRUST, HELP THE HOSPICES
AND PARKINSON'S UK

Janet's Garden

Christine at Appletreewick

Birthday cake at
Mistletoe Lodge

Mrs Marren
then and now

Ruth with Bill Murray

Ruth's Dad
dressed up for
the garden opening
at Appletreewick

They opened the garden to the public for the National Gardens Scheme in June 2013 for the first time and as the first garden in the town ever to do so. Janet decided to go just that little bit further. "I always squeeze as much creativity as I can out of an opportunity – so I contacted a number of artists and makers to invite them to exhibit, and held a 'Secret Craft Fair'. We were delighted to have around 350 visitors over the weekend. People enjoyed the garden, the teas and the cakes and I spent a lot of time talking to folk about the garden. People were really pleased to find art and craft in the garden and the relaxed atmosphere made it easy for people to chat with the artists about their work and buy gifts and treats for their homes and gardens. Since then I've built a group up so there are now four gardens that open for the NGS, each with a different special interest – bee-keeping in one, tortoises in another."

The shed at the bottom of the garden is also utilised as part of the Secret Craft Fair. Janet tells me about her equally creative brother Martin who's exhibited in there a couple of times. "He started making ray guns out of stuff he found and it grew and grew until he'd made quite a collection. He has a story for each one and put a travelling exhibition together. He's got a wonderful dry wit and he would stand there looking quite imposing in vaguely military costume and with a perfectly straight face explaining what these things were."

I am sad this funny guy isn't here with us in the garden as Janet continues " So he kicked the ball off for us having something a bit unusual in the shed each year, one artist took it over as a tiny cinema, others as a fairy den; it's been a pottery where visitors can throw something on the wheel, and a place for ecology and sustainability projects to promote themselves from. I'm always on the look out for something creative, curious and interesting for the shed". If that isn't a reason to visit this garden's Secret Craft Fair next year I don't know what is.

When I visit Janet and Pete on this Saturday in May, they have a small working party here as part of a national gardening project called Growzones. Janet explains, "There are five or six households in our local group, and each spring and again each autumn, we take it in turns to spend Saturday mornings in one of the gardens – so you get about 12 hours of person-power in a morning from the group." The gardens can be small or large but all get the same amount of hours from members. "We didn't know each other before," says Janet. For her, Growzones was a way of meeting more neighbours after years of commuting out of the area during the day. She also wanted a bit of help in the garden. "Then the Growzones leaflet came from Caroline and that was a good start," she says.

Caroline, who is working with us in the sunny garden as we chat says, "I made some flyers and put them through the doors down the street and waited to see who turned up to the first meeting. For a Growzone session we work in the garden and then we have lunch, everyone brings something to share for lunch and a lot of it is home-grown because there is a lot of veg growing in the group."

And after a not very tiring morning helping in the garden – many hands making very light work indeed – Willy and I are lucky enough to share lunch with them. Janet has made the most delicious soup. "I try to find really simple recipes using food we've grown," she says, and it may be simple but it is really gorgeous.

Sam is another of the Growzones team and tells me over lunch that "Gardening is my time for some peace when the children are off doing their thing. There is a connection which is grounding and even if you're tired it makes you feel better."

Growzones sounds like a really wonderful way of meeting people, learning about gardening with fellow amateur gardeners and growing a social life at the same time as getting help in your garden. Another brilliant idea – why didn't I think of that?

Jewels and Mark's Garden

I decide to stay close to home the third week of May because it's a time of family birthdays and the Daisybus and I need a little relaxation after our long journeys hither and thither. So this week a Herefordshire garden first and later in the week a Worcestershire garden.

Jewels Peplow-Williams is another arty type who combines her garden opening with an art exhibition. Jewels makes beautiful porcelain bits and pieces. Although she lives in Herefordshire, not very far from me at all, I hadn't visited her before, and as I drive up in the Daisybus I'm excited to spot another VW in the garage on the corner. Turns out her husband Mark owns the garage with his brother and father and they specialise in VWs! I can almost feel Daisy sigh with relief because I hadn't as yet found a specialist for her and I know she needs one.

The excitement of finding a VW garage is only increased on walking into Jewels' home and garden. Again, not a huge garden but so so beautifully done – and a house from my dreams – wooden slats and glass – wonderfully light inside and lots of doors opening out onto the garden with its stunning centrepiece, the pond, surrounded with decking to complement the wood of the house. Absolutely my kind of place.

The land at the back of the house rises to a terrace from where, on this sunny day, the Herefordshire countryside sparkles for miles in front of us. This is the reason Jewels bought the house and turned her hand to making the rest of the garden. Like me, although living in the middle of the country, Jewels has a love of the sea and her porcelain often depicts the horizons of the seascape. Her pieces, divine in their subtle simplicity, are made in her studio overlooking the garden which she says provides the tranquillity for her to work. "Art is all about creating a sensation, a feeling, emotion – and gardens do the same," she says, "the garden is an extension of my creativity."

Having married the man next door after moving in, Jewels now enjoys working together with Mark in the garden. "It's so restful and makes me so happy," she tells me. They've created a stunning natural pond with perfect complementary planting around the edges and a hidden garden the other end. This is the first year they are opening the garden for the NGS and they've invited seven other artists to display their work in the house over that weekend so there's lots to be done. As a special birthday treat for Willy I've insisted he takes a day off work and helps me instead! We both enjoy tackling a weedy bank in the late May sunshine in a far corner of the garden at Mistletoe Lodge. As a reward, Jewels has made Willy a fabulous birthday cake that we all eat on the pier over the pond together with Jewels' daughters, just home from school. This is a beautiful moment that will stay with me for a long time and, as a bonus, we're home in time to pick and eat supper in our own garden for a change.

Ruth's Garden

Back in February I met Ruth Edwards at our NGS County Meeting. Immediately likeable with her friendly Welsh accent and sense of humour, Ruth invited me to visit her garden that she is opening for the first time this year, so I pop round, not very far, but to a part of Worcestershire I've not visited before. It feels like the other side of the country rather than the same county.

Having recently been thinking about people gardening to honour their ancestors, I realise I have met in Ruth someone who has put her heart into rescuing and reviving the garden dreams of a lady she didn't even know.

Ruth tells me she is a 'hostie' on a private jet and that gardening is quite literally a relaxing healing break from her jet-set lifestyle. Anyone less like a typical gardener I've never met. Impeccably dressed and made-up even in her gardening clothes, Ruth completely destroys my excuse for having hands that look like hen's feet ("I'm a gardener") though she admits that she has to work at it. Embarrassed about my own hands, I say that they've probably been washed and scrubbed about ten times more than any normal person who hasn't tried to run a B&B and be a gardener at the same time. You just can't serve a Full English with dirt under your nails.

But, as unlikely a gardener as she looks, Ruth is totally hooked and enthusiastically shows me around. "People don't understand it until they do it," she says, and we agree that sometimes it feels like gardening is an in-joke – you only get it when you do it – it's impossible to explain how it makes you feel. In this garden though, it is not just Ruth's emotions that are important. Two other women are often on her mind.

Ruth, who is also a talented photographer, tells me "I went to visit Mrs Warren – the old lady who planted the garden – about four years ago. I got so much enjoyment from photographing the flowers she'd planted that I asked my neighbour where she'd moved to so I could meet her and show her the photographs. She was in a retirement village and I introduced myself as someone who had bought her house. I hadn't bought it off her. Another couple bought it from her and we from them. I had taken my photos to show her and that's when I found out she was now blind..."

Ruth asked Mrs Warren if she'd like to come back to visit the house and garden "She was delighted as she couldn't get out much."

"She couldn't see individual flowers but she could see shapes and was amazed at how wide and high the conifers she'd planted had grown. She said 'If I had realised they were going to grow so big, I wouldn't have planted them like that.. so close together.'

My husband had kept asking me to get rid of all the big trees that were crowding out the light and each time I refused but when I returned from taking her back to her home I had decided to finally remove them... Her comments changed my thinking, as she had been the original planner."

"I hadn't ever thought about opening my garden for the NGS but I responded to an article by the County Organiser and when we were accepted I thought how lovely it would be to tell Mrs Warren. I thought she would be delighted. So I rang her and the line was dead. I checked several avenues and couldn't find her... I feared she might have died and would never have had the joy of knowing. Finally my neighbour tracked her down via someone who used to work for her and was able to tell me that she was now in a nursing home in Bromsgrove. I went straight away to visit her and tell her. I was so happy to know she was still around...

When I saw her she said 'I am old, I'm crippled, I'm useless now' but I was able to tell her that, the garden she designed and worked so hard on was going to be visited by hundreds of people who'd benefit from walking around it and that itself will benefit several charities…

Her memory has practically failed her now so I rang the staff a week before and asked if they could possibly bring her. She was our first visitor and the memories came flooding back. I told her that many people got great pleasure from her garden and we gave her some apple juice made from the apple trees she planted."

Ruth tells me that Mrs Warren, now blind and quite deaf, wept tears of joy at returning to the garden she started. In Ruth's visitors book she wrote "I'll be 99 next month and this is the best present I could have. We were very happy here."

And there's another lady who appreciates Ruth's generosity with her garden. Ruth tells me about her as we sit at the top of the garden in an area she has named Eleanor's Vintage Garden with its old mangle, tin bath and washing line complete with old long johns.

"I know Christine from church. She is a sweet lady who has had a lot of suffering in her life, losing her daughter and grandson in a fire. She gave me an old mangle and I decided to name a part of the garden after her, but she asked me to call it Ellie's Garden in memory of her daughter. It was so she wouldn't worry if she didn't come through the operation on her back last winter. I knew she had put flowers on her daughter's grave every 5 December and in 2014 she couldn't because she was undergoing a huge and critical operation on her back. I felt she was more concerned about no one being there to remember her daughter than she was about her own health.

"I wanted her to have something to look forward to when she finally came out of hospital. She had just lost her husband too and so we decided after the operation she'd come to visit me, to see Eleanor's Vintage Garden and we'd sup pink champagne together... something she'd never, ever done in her life.."

"And it was one of the first things she did after two and a half months in a coma. Even though she wasn't supposed to climb steps yet (and was on morphine, so shouldn't have really had any alcohol) she was determined to come and spend some time here with me in the garden, remembering her beloved daughter. Her daughter had been deaf and as we couldn't finish the champagne, we popped the cork back in and Christine held the bottle in the car. On the journey back, the cork popped off and hit Christine hard on the ear! It made us laugh and laugh because it was uncanny that we had just toasted Ellie who was deaf."

Ruth's warmth and kindness move me enormously. I'm filled with hope that the world is full of Ruths who will make this planet a better place to live.

"It gives me pleasure that bits of my garden are dedicated to other people," Ruth says, "like my knitted apple tree by Barbara." She points to an old tree whose branches are encased in tubes of stripey colourful knitted wool. It looks like a giant hand in a fingerless glove. It's crazy but fabulous.

The garden has a pond and Ruth tells me, "I collect pebbles from beaches all over the world, which I place in my pond. I also have sand from some of the best beaches and even a buoy which Bill Murray's son gave to me while visiting his holiday home and private beach on Martha's Vineyard."

The blue buoy hangs with others near some blue hydrangeas outside her pretty whitewashed shed "I got inspiration from Massachusetts where there is a lot of this. They have to keep their gardens neat there or the council sends someone round to do it instead and sends them the bill!"

A sunnier, kinder person you couldn't meet. Ruth's love for and empathy with the other women in her garden's life, fill the place with meaning and despite the poignant stories, joy.

Ros & Ros's Garden

As it was Willy's birthday this week I take him to his favourite garden, Moors Meadow, owned by our friend Ros Bissell. Ros and her mum garden this romantic place alone which, as it is on a steep slope and her mum is over 90, is quite something. But it is their passion for plants that keeps them going strong. Ros tells us:

"In 1955 my parents, Rosie and Tom Johnson, moved to Moors Meadow, a long-derelict house and seven acres of fields on a north facing hillside overlooking the Kyre valley. With hard work, no money and a hungry young family they ran it as a smallholding and market garden."

"My parents' love of plants was soon evident and as the chicks flew the nest their green-fingered passion blossomed. With Dad's expertise at propagation many of the now-mature trees and shrubs started as tiny seeds in his hands."

As the years passed the fencing was gradually moved to allow more room for the garden and less for the reduced number of Jersey cows and ultimately the decision was made to stop keeping animals.

"In 1999 I, the youngest of the family, returned home when Mum was on her own and between us we quickly set about removing the remaining stock fences and creating new areas of garden throughout the whole seven acres. With a plethora of ideas and an abundance of energy the garden rapidly evolved into the resemblance of what it is today. Features, furniture and sculptures were created using mostly whatever materials were at hand therefore a minimum was spent on the hardscaping thus allowing the acquisition of more plants."

In the garden there are also seats and sculptures forged by Ros's late husband, Dave Bissell, along with sculptures created by other local blacksmiths.

Ros admits "We're self-confessed rabid plantaholics – we were always on the lookout for rarely seen species and soon amassed a vast collection to include grasses, ferns, bulbs, perennials, climbers, shrubs and trees from around the world."

Gardening has certainly helped their health and fitness and Ros says, "From the farming days and through all the gardening years we have remained organic in the knowledge that any chemical use is detrimental to the environment and ultimately our own health. This has gone a long way to ensuring an abundance of wildlife and Mum's ability to continue gardening long into her 90s" and to me the two women seem especially happy people – always smiling, always willing to share a plant. They have always been our local gardening heroes. Once voted the most romantic garden in the country, Moors Meadow is certainly a favourite of ours and a good note on which to take a short break from my Daisybus travels and jump on a train to Paris with my sister and niece…

In Montmartre the scenery as in the rest of Paris, is almost entirely man-made and being a country girl and a gardener at heart, I am naturally drawn towards the multi-coloured, multi-textured, multi-fragranced pockets of joy that are the fleuristes. I move closer and breathe deeply and hang around the displays of blooms as though I were a bee attracted to my source of life.

An afternoon in the Jardin de Tuilleries restores my floral equilibrium where the mixed reds and pinks of the summer borders complement the green lawns, colonnades of trees and grandeur of the peoples' palaces. Posters announce '2015 Jardins, Jardin' a garden festival and I remember I have my 'Daisybus Festival Season' to look forward to when we get home.

The Floral Fringe Fair

I had tried to visit Ned Mersey, a composer, while in Sussex, Sadly our diaries didn't have matching windows (as those of us who carry briefcases say) so I asked him if he would write to me and tell me how his garden influences his music. Turns out he's a

Viscount and it's rather more than a garden – it's Bignor Park, and I'm relieved I didn't have to go in case I was meant to curtsey or only speak when spoken to or something. I probably needn't have worried because he sounds very nice.... And this is what he said

"The gardens at Bignor Park provide a great inspiration for my orchestral and choral composition. First, because in the late eighteenth century the celebrated early romantic poet, Charlotte Smith, used to wander among them. Bignor Park was her family home and I have set one of her sonnets to music. Secondly because no one can fail to be inspired by the panoramic views across to the South Downs, looming above us with no sign of habitation, and sometimes it feels like we could be on another continent. I think of Edward Elgar and Hilaire Belloc and am not surprised that this part of Sussex provided such fertile material for their imaginations. More intimately, the windy bowers and dark wooden dells contrast with the man-made box hedges and lawns and give a great sense of the balance between nature and humanity's wish to control it. The words of Charlotte Smith resound in my ears:

> *Low murmurs creep along the woody vale,*
> *The tremulous Aspens shudder in the breeze,*
> *Slow o'er the downs the leaden vapours sail,*
> *While I, beneath these old paternal trees,*
> *Mark the dark shadows of the threaten'd storm,*
> *As gathering clouds o'erveil the morning sun;*

We arrive in Sussex the night before the Floral Fringe Fair and have been offered a room at Lesley Chamberlain's home in Findon. Lesley is the Assistant County Organiser for the Sussex NGS, which consistently raises incredibly high sums of money for the charities. There are a lot of gardens in Sussex and a lot of people and the volunteers for the NGS in the county really have their work cut out. Lesley also runs her own garden design and consultancy company and lectures in clubs, village halls and cruise ships. I like Lesley's straightforward attitude and can see how she is the sort of person who gets things done. Her own hidden garden is small and perfectly accomplished as befits a good garden designer and her home is a welcome retreat at the end of our long journey. Asking where we can eat, Lesley tells us about three places to eat in the village, a nice local pub, an Indian restaurant and another place "that does tall food". I am puzzled and ask her what she means by tall food. "You know when they stack it up in a pile in the middle of the plate," she says. I love that.

Few people are so dedicated to wildlife gardening that they will put on a whole festival for it but that's what Jean Jackman did. In fact, she gave herself The Floral Fringe Fair as a 60th birthday present and kindly invited me and my Daisybus along to promote the NGS, for whom she also opens her private garden. Jean describes the festival, held annually in the grounds of Knepp Castle in Sussex, as 'an eclectic, quirky, foodie, arty, plantaholics wildlife event with a vintage twist'. So what's not to like? And as festivals are second homes to VW campervans I obviously have to go. I bundle up lots of jolly bunting, buy a bright flowery canopy and gather together all my nicest garden props to make a pretty display. I pack my Anna trousers, a bandana and cheesecloth shirt, so that I can look the part with the bus and compete in the vintage fancy dress competition. I also drag along Willy who was after all one of the original 70s hippies, so my authentication is assured.

I arranged to meet Brian Barnes on the Saturday of the Festival which was silly because I wasn't there till the Sunday. Remember I am not a professional at all this….. Anyhow Brian kindly told me by letter about his wife Hilary and their garden not so far away in Storrington.

"My wife Hilary died on the 16th July 2014 from cancer – Gardening had been her religion for her whole life and she was recognised nationally when receiving two awards, The Daily Mail Gardener of the Year in 2006 and the BBC Gardener of the Year in 2009.

We were lucky in being able to keep Hil at home, giving her the chance to see her creation to the end. This was due to the incredible work that the Macmillan nurses did, installing a bed in the sitting room so that Hil could look out of the French windows at her garden."

My Anna trousers are my favourite trousers. I've had them since June 2000 when Anna and Niall Robson were married in our garden in the Cotswolds. Anna, same age as me, was Willy's niece and the four of us had become great friends and spent many wonderful times getting a little drunk and laughing together at our home and theirs. It was a huge honour when they asked if they could have their wedding reception in our garden and the sight of Anna walking with her father down the aisle of white rambling roses over our pergola is one my most beautiful memories. We grew our earliest crop of sweet peas for the couple and had to cover them with fleece the night before the wedding when we were threatened with a late frost.

Tall, blonde, beautiful and effortlessly funky, only three years later Anna told us she had breast cancer and after a seven year battle she died leaving a huge hole in all our lives. Macmillan Nurses helped the family at the end and they are one of the reasons I am such a devoted NGS supporter. Anna, like a lot of women, fought with everything she had, including her fabulous sense of humour. Despite us all being terrified of her going, our times together were mostly full of tears of laughter rather than sorrow. Leaving her husband and her daughter, Loulou, was, of course, her biggest source of grief and as brave as anyone can be, the constant pain and fear of the illness together with the thought of the hurt that loss brings to those you love is hard to live with every day.

Knowing she was not going to see her daughter grow into a woman was, of course, the worst thing of all.

Anna and I had many chats over those years and we emailed most days, right up to the last. She supported me when I lost my little girl and I tried to support her knowing she was leaving her little girl. We often talked about the unfairness of it all – I used to wish I could swap with her; that it was me that was dying for then I could be with my daughter and Anna could be well and stay with her daughter. Life doesn't work like that though, does it? But Anna once said to me, "I'd rather be in my position than yours." She knew and loved her daughter and had spent happy years with her – not enough – but some, and she wouldn't change that for the world. She would rather have had that time than no time at all. I've often thought I want to tell Loulou what her mother said to me that day. Maybe this is my way of telling her.

Anna's trousers are the trousers she gave me as thanks for hosting their wedding. She had worn a similar pair for their Register Office ceremony and I had coveted them loudly. White flares, skin-tight from the knee up, with a pale blue embroidered silk finish at the bottom of the legs. Stretchy, with a side zip, they're reassuringly flattering – I probably wear them too much and I dread them falling to pieces.

Anyhow, perfect methinks for the Floral Fringe Fair and indeed I am asked – I don't have to push myself forward, note – to take part in the vintage dress competition and I think, 'hey I've got this in the bag!'

Lined up with my competitors, the judge looks us all over carefully. She spends a lot of time looking at me – looking me up and down – I feel a win coming. But she chooses someone else. I am of course magnanimous in defeat and walk away from the group of photographers around the winner back to my Daisybus and get a cuddle of commiseration from Willy. Standing back he says, "You look great" but he too looks me up and down and then he says, "What is that?" and points at the top of my legs. I look down and the blood rushes to my face "Omigod" I shriek and leap into the back of my bus.

"What the hell?"

"Have you wet yourself?" Willy says.

"Of course I haven't wet myself – I think I'd know if I'd wet myself!"

But the evidence is there – a big wet patch in between my legs. But it's not wet. I just don't understand it. How could I not have noticed this huge stain on my favourite trousers?

I change, half-crouching awkwardly in the back of Daisybus, into my jeans and take a closer look.

"Ugh Sarah, what ARE you doing?" says Willy

"I recognise this smell" I say with my Anna trousers to my face.

"Eugh, puhleease!" he says, and we both laugh.

"No, no no no – it's, oooh what is it – oooh I KNOW this," I continue and finally it dawns that it's coconut oil. I haven't worn them since we went to France and my coconut oil jar broke in the case on the way home. I hadn't even noticed it had got on my trousers and apparently it seems coconut oil doesn't come out in one wash. I am gutted and cringe for the rest of the day at the thought of me proudly standing there in the vintage line-up with a huge 'wet patch' visible to everyone watching. The surrounding spectators' smiles and laughter now take on a whole different meaning. On the bright side though, I totally accept that an incontinent hippy can't be allowed to win the vintage fancy dress prize, so maybe there is some dignity to be had in failure after all? Anna might have laughed so much she really would have wet herself.

The first thing the four of us talked about when we used to meet up was what was going on in our gardens. Mostly we loved the same things and were always recommending plants to each other, but one thing Anna and Niall would not budge on was orange. Orange was allowed no place in their garden, in the same way that celery was never allowed in their cooking. I kind of agree about the celery – apart from soup – but orange roses are some of my favourites. They always seem to be the ones that smell the best and fragrance is so important in a garden to me. Whilst I could live with a very structured formal garden of clipped and topiarised evergreens visually, I'm not sure I could live without the smells that come from the messiness of flowers. Anna and Nially's wedding was for me a real celebration of gardens and flowers as well as the huge love between them and I like to think the setting of our first garden helped spread that love among all of their friends and family.

Geoffrey's Garden

If I was to marry again I think I might very well choose Matara in Gloucestershire as my perfect garden location. Driving back into the Cotswolds again the stone still feels like home to me even twelve years after leaving. The weather has changed on this day at the beginning of June and I visit Matara Gardens of Wellbeing in the pouring rain. Nevertheless entering the cloistered courtyard I feel sheltered and peaceful and an almost meditative state descends as I wander around the private gardens around the house with their unusual Costwoldian-Oriental fusion planting. I can see some fabulous wedding day photo opportunities. "Marriages are conducted here with open-hearted individuality," owner Geoffrey Higgins says, "It is important that couples have a wedding expressing love in their own unique way."

The extended gardens are made of meandering paths and clearings, a labyrinth, a healing spiral, woodlands and parkland with art works and thoughtful and thought-provoking plaques with invitations to become at one with the beauty of it all. I like the idea of the barefoot trail and may as well be barefoot as I am wearing completely unsuitable footwear and am soaked to the toes anyway.

The Blue Zone walk through the trees teaches principles of wellbeing from around the world. It tells me there are five Blue Zones in the world where people live longest. People in these zones nurture social networks, eat a plant-based diet moderately and do daily natural activity. I particularly liked this little notice:

"The world's longest-lived people don't run marathons or join gyms….Instead they live in environments that constantly nudge

Matara

Anne's Art

Flowery trousers
at Hellens

Hellens Garden Festival

The truly
amazing
Dame
Margaret
Anstee

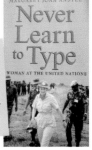

Never Learn to Type
MARGARET JOAN ANSTEE
A WOMAN AT THE UNITED NATIONS

Hub friends at Stockton Bury Gardens

Tobyfest

Middle Ninfa

them into moving without thinking about it. They grow gardens and don't have mechanical conveniences for house and yard work." See, I told you gardening is good for you.

Geoffrey says the place "is dedicated to the full expression of the human spirit and a deeper relationship with nature." It is the realisation of a dream he and his wife June had when they arrived here. It is important to him that they are not imposing their will but doing everything with love and care. Even in this torrential rain I am very much at peace in this wonderful place and slightly regret that it is too wet for me to help in the garden and spend longer here. As I drive out, it is the sign at the gate 'Matara Gardens of Wellbeing' that inspires a name for this book.

But my peace is disturbed as I drive home by the gusts bombarding the Daisybus. In the squally wind, the trees I pass remind me of Marilyn Monroe, with their skirts blown up to reveal legs-like tree trunks.

Richard's Garden

I'm constantly amazed at how the British weather is so changeable – especially how it can change through many temperatures and levels of humidity within just one day. Thank goodness for that – with so much rain it would be hard to live without the hope of a brighter day. At least we British are able to be ever-optimistic. The day following my wet visit to Matara turns out to be utterly glorious and to make things even better I am heading up into the Welsh hills above Abergavenny – an absolute favourite area of mine.

The Daisybus pulls us slowly – really slowly – up the hills that I feel are rising up to greet me, towards Middle Ninfa Farm. I'm glad Willy has come along too, in case we start rolling backwards. I don't know what he can actually do if we start rolling backwards, but safety in numbers and all that. We are greeted with confusion by Rohan Lewis as husband Richard has completely forgotten he's invited me. "Never mind", says Rohan, "he'll be back soon, have a look round the garden." So we do. Richard soon pulls up in his tennis gear with a young French WOOFer (an organisation that connects people who want to live and learn on organic farms) who is staying to help on the farm for a while.

Sharing their lunch with us in the sunshine, Richard and Rohan tell us about their interesting lives spent living and working abroad and the numerous social projects they've been involved with, from growing tea and limes with smallholders in Africa to borstals and city farms in the UK. Richard has enjoyed working with land and people all his working life and continues to do so now on this idyllic hillside in Wales by opening Middle Ninfa to visitors. As well as opening the gardens for the NGS, they have a bunkhouse and a campsite and people who stay are welcome to pick vegetables and salad from his large vegetable garden. Apart from the main campsite there are six further remote sites with their own special characteristics; Stone Circle, which occupies a terrace behind an ancient stone wall; Dixe's has room for just one single tent in a shallow dip in the land; Deri (which means oak in Welsh); Skirrid View; Small Leaved Lime and Forest Pitch. Difficult to choose between them methinks and wonders how much of a faff it would be to stay six nights and move the tent from one pitch to another so as to experience the character of each unique spot.

As we speak about land and growing, recycling and composting and I start veering off into my evangelical enthusiasms I realise Richard is more of an eco-whisperer than an eco-warrior. He is happy to show people what he is doing here but he is not a proselytiser; he likes to demonstrate not lecture. I can see what an asset he has been to the organisations he has worked with and realise how they would probably tire of me very quickly indeed.

Willy and I spend a lovely afternoon clearing Richard's waterfall of weeds. It is warm and the views from here are stunning. I don't want to be anywhere else in the world and I am blissfully happy. When we leave, Richard reminds me: "If you want to be happy for an hour, get drunk – if you want to be happy for a day, get married – if you want to be happy for life, plant a garden." Never a truer word spoken.

Rolling back downhill actually turned out to be scarier than struggling uphill as the Daisybus engine doesn't like idling, which is all I was asking of her. She cuts out unless you keep the revs up and keeping the revs up and braking at the same time is quite a tricky thing. I soon found out I couldn't rely on the handbrake entirely either. So it was as painful a roaring first gear all the way down as it had been a brave straining first gear uphill. But just as beautiful. We drive back via Skenfrith, passing a sign to somewhere called Dawn of the Day which we agree we must visit next time we come over to stay at The Bell, one of our favourite places. I'm seeing many interesting and enticing name places on my travels – some less enticing, more ghoulishly fascinating like Flesh Hovel Lane and Warning Tongue Lane but all provide mildly entertaining ways to spend driving time wondering how on earth the name came about.

Margaret's Garden

The counties where Wales and England meet that we call The Welsh Marches have some of the prettiest scenery in Britain. Lots of hills, lots of trees, farmhouses and cottages, tumbling rivers, castle ruins and cosy pubs. So it's not a hardship for me to offer to drive from one part of the Marches to another to give Margaret Anstee a hand with her Walled Garden at Knill. Little do I know as I enjoy the journey that I am about to meet one of the most extraordinary women this country has produced. She hasn't even hinted at her past in her invitation to me, telling me only that she will be 89 in June and on top of arthritis has pulmonary fibrosis and has to be almost permanently on oxygen. This is obviously making it extremely difficult for her to keep on top of her garden. Not helped by the fact that her wonderful gardener has recently had a terrible car crash and can no longer do heavy garden work. So – Daisybus to the rescue!

Well, as it turns out, it's a very big beautiful walled garden with a long, wide bog garden running down one side to meet the river at the bottom and I am only here for one afternoon. Margaret shows me the bits that need most attention and I immediately get stuck in and weed as fast as I can. I hit on the idea of leaving piles of weeds on the lawn for someone else to tidy up later so that I can crack on – great excuse – and I thoroughly enjoy working away in the sunshine in this amazing place. Everyone loves a walled garden don't they? There is something so very romantic about old walls, often, as here, covered in old roses. Margaret and her aunt fell in love with the place when they first saw it on a frosty walk on Christmas Day 1979. When it became available in 1987 they bought it and it was her aunt's home until her death in 2000.

Margaret insists that I stop to have lunch with her in the garden room even though I say I am happy to carry on working. I am glad I do stop because it is then that I begin to discover what an amazing woman I am sitting opposite. A proper writer would possibly have done some research before going, but I admit, to me, she is simply another gardener and good egg that opens her garden for the NGS.

But Dame Margaret Anstee has done so much in her lifetime, something I discover mostly after I leave through reading the autobiography she kindly signs and gives me to take away. A quick glance at the back cover before lunch shows praise for the book from people like Kofi Annan, Jimmy Carter and Boutros Boutros Ghali. I feel gauche and inadequate, so retrench to the safety of talking about gardens, but the safety is short-lived as Margaret surprises me by telling me her favourite garden is the one she made on a promontory above Lake Titicaca. I barely know where Lake Titicaca is……. South America somewhere I'm thinking… but it is clear that Margaret knows and loves it well. Villa Margarita is, she says, in one of the most beautiful places in the world which is why, of all the places in the world she has lived and worked, she chose this spot above a lake in Bolivia to be her retirement home. The garden has been tamed from its wildness by Inca-style stone terraces, and hanging gardens that cascade down to the lake shore. Much of the vegetation is the natural cacti and wild plants but apparently roses do well, even at 14,000 feet above sea-level, and many birds flock to this small oasis. She tells how after a day of writing she would clamber breathlessly up the hills behind the house to watch the reflection of the setting sun suffuse the majestic peaks of rose and gold. Living high up a Bolivian mountain is sadly now impossible for Margaret who needs oxygen almost constantly supplied by machine even here in the Welsh Marches where she now lives.

In her book, Margaret tells of a garden party at the Walled Garden in Knill: "In 1996, when the garden was spick and span, ready for its summer opening, we decided to give a garden birthday party on 25 June. Our guests were a medley of farmers, country neighbours, diplomats, journalists and even two ambassadors – of Bolivia and Angola. The garden shone at its best – roses, delphiniums and clematis against the rosy brick walls, long reaches of candelabra primulas blooming in the bog garden and heavenly scents wafting on the breeze. The guests wandered through the gardens, drinks in hand, before lunch in a flower-decked marquee. Down by the river a band of itinerant Bolivian musicians struck up in the shade of the weeping willows on their traditional instruments – quena, charango, zampona. They wore the typical dress of Potosi: homespun trousers, round white hats, brightly garlanded, waistcoats and ponchos of rainbow hue. Their plangent Andean music blended perfectly with the gentle hills of the Welsh Marches, a landscape so distant and so much more verdant than the frugal vistas of the altiplano and the encircling snowy peaks that inspired it."

Working for the UN for over forty years (itself impressive for a woman from her era), Margaret was the first woman to rise to the rank of Under-Secretary-General and has spent her life peacekeeping and rebuilding communities across the world after war. Much has been written about her and I am truly not worthy or able to do her justice here. Having been at the heart of world affairs for fifty years, she has achieved so much more than anyone else I know and I am humbled to meet her and receive her heartfelt thanks for a little bit of weeding. Most of us want to see peace in the world and some of us know this will only ever be possible if poverty and oppression are eliminated, but this lady has spent her life actually out there trying to make that happen. I would love Margaret even if she didn't have a fab garden.

After a few days on home territory I'm setting off up the country again, leaving lovely Worcestershire to drive north through Shropshire to the glorious Peak District. Driving along the country lanes of the Peaks I feel as though I am driving on top of the world. I have stunning views all around and not just because I'm up in the Daisybus. The country lanes here are not hidden in deep hedges like ours, so anyone in a normal car gets the same incredible views and I wonder how anyone gets anywhere on time with such beauty to linger over. I'm looking for the Wild Boar Inn, where I can camp overnight. Right on the road it's not the prettiest of pubs but the welcome and the views more than make up for that. In the cosy bar an early customer is watching Johnny Kingdom on the telly and it feels so homely I could settle quite happily here for the evening, but the landlord tells me he's not serving food tonight and recommends The Hanging Gate, not far away. I drag myself away from the fire and hope The Hanging Gate is friendlier than it sounds. It is – though they're not serving tonight either – but it was worth the visit for the view from the car park. I'm beginning to wish I'd picked up a garage sandwich up way back in civilisation, but there's no chance of a shop or garage open at this time for miles around. As I walk back to the Daisybus a car pulls up alongside me. It's the customer from The Wild Boar. "Here's some breakfast for you," he says, and passes me some eggs from the passenger seat of his car. "How thoughtful of you – that's lovely, thank you." I am so touched that he has followed me just to be kind that I don't like to tell him that I have no stove in the bus and can't cook a thing.

I'm directed next to the Lyle Arms, which appears to be where everyone in the know goes on this Monday evening. A lively pub with lovely staff; it's not long before I am settled with a brandy and a pasta bake: Happiness in deep high country.

Anne's Garden

Next day I head down into Sale to meet Anne Earnshaw, an artist who tells me her garden is her inspiration for her work. Anne has been gardening for thirty years and she's had a lot to cope with in that time with two near fatal car-crashes, a broken relationship and the loss of her mother. Her current art is photographing water really close up and she tells me, "I think the feelings I get when I am near water are quite spiritual and I felt this when my mum died. Around all of nature itself too, with trees especially – from looking at or touching a blade of grass to watching the movement of clouds – it's very inspirational."

"Mum died at the start of my 3rd year on my Visual Arts Degree and wow this was hard," she continues. "I carried on, as I was determined to finish it. My subject matter was always Nature and then I was drawn more to water and its movement. The grieving process was plain to see in my art work and the work from that when I look back was amazing. The body of work was just enormous. I have kept it all and in years to come will be interesting to look at. I think my degree show should have been called ' Where Has Mum Gone?' I was looking for her. I am a Christian and I could feel her presence." Anne shows me an image she captured when a white feather floated in front of her while she was hoping for a sign from her mother. "The Feather Image was a lovely surprise," she says.

Anne's gardening and her art are intimately linked. "My love for gardening and art has been my passion throughout my life and has helped me through many ups and downs, no matter what challenges come my way health-wise or otherwise. It is very therapeutic and helps me to relax and show my artistic flare in many ways."

Anne tells me about the car accidents she experienced as a passenger and the description of one will stay with me forever… "We were so lucky to come out alive from that experience – the car rolled over and over just like in a movie and we ended up in front of a tanker lorry being pushed along backwards. Gary and I were talking to each other as it was all happening. It could have all gone another way that day and I feel so lucky that there was no one next to us in the third lane or the embankment was higher not lower and especially that the French lorry driver kept his cool and slowed us down by gently braking as we were looking at him head on . You wake up and you don't know what a day can bring."

Laughing, she then tells me, "Oh and after that I got run over when I wasn't thinking straight – and that just put the icing on the cake. That day I did say WHY ME?! to my husband as I was crying non-stop, lying on the floor with a dead leg and a pool of blood from my head injury."

Anne admits "Depression can easily set in at times like these and you cannot function as you used to. I love aerobics and dancing and these were off the agenda for a while and then, guess what, you put on weight, get fed up etc etc… I did eventually get my old self back with a lot of hard work – mind and body working together. I do have to look after myself and I can be reminded by my whiplash sometimes if I don't stretch, walk and keep myself active. I was able to help myself get better after learning about alternative medicines like cranial osteopathy and homeopathic/skeleton alignment treatments."

Seeing her walking around her garden chatting and smiling with me today, you would never guess what this lady has been through. I wonder whether a healthy obsession (or perhaps it's better called devotion) to a subject can be healing in itself. Whether it's horses,

Porsches or roses – photography, painting or gardening – it's about becoming absorbed in something other than our own problems. Naval gazing gets really boring after a while.

Moving on, we talk about the spring flowers in her garden. "Names are not important to me," she says. "It's when they flower, their colour and structure that interest me." And, like Alison Pollock in Yorkshire, she places her colour thoughtfully. "Clashes bug me!" she says. "Bright colours shock and awaken but I need calmer colours at the moment."

And inspiration comes from other gardens too. Arley Hall nearby is her favourite place and she has spent a lot of time working on projects for her art there. Having spent a nice morning in her own garden she suggests we get in our cars and go there now. So we do.

Over tea and cake at Arley, Anne tells me that with a proper job too she mostly gardens in the evenings alone and talks to her plants as she works. "It is loving work and I love it – it's nurturing and it teaches patience."

"Ideas come from other places like this, but I tend not to copy, just let them swirl around in my head for a while and they come out in a different way – it's about how I want it to feel."

We walk around the famously beautiful gardens of Arley and I am gratified to see in the leaflet that the owners believe that it is 'a wonderful example of the idea that the best gardens are living, changing works of art.' No wonder Anne is happy here.

The garden's best-known feature is its massive herbaceous border apparently the first border of its kind planted in England. We meet one of the gardeners and I ask how they keep it looking so incredibly good. Do they not have any pest or disease problems? He tells me that the whole garden is walled or fenced to keep out rabbits, which also means other beneficial small animals like hedgehogs are kept inside the walls. Hedgehogs are cared for as much as the plants here: the gardeners leave piles of dead stuff in the borders all over the winter and mark them with a stick if a hedgehog is in residence. The marked piles won't get tidied away until the hedgehogs are up and about in the spring. With lots of Mistle thrushes living there they have no need for slug pellets.

It is really heart-warming to know that one of the oldest, biggest and best gardens in the country has no interest in old-fashioned chemical gardening and I'm also so pleased that Anne, after all she's been through, can find such peace and happiness here. It's a place to lose herself in nature and her art. Her parting message to me is, "I pray and meditate when I can and when I don't spend time in my garden, walking or doing my art, I can feel the difference. Life can be overwhelming at times, it can be joyful with lots of surprise – good and bad. I have learned to make the most of it and enjoy life with a smile. We just have to 'Keep Going', which is my motto!"

And with that I climb back into the Daisybus and 'Keep Going' too – heading for my next campsite. But the weather turns and I get lost again and when it starts raining too I start to get really cold, so when I see the Marton Arms in the village of Thornton in Lonsdale, I guiltily decide to check myself in to a warm room with a bathroom and a hot meal in the bar.

Over breakfast I chat with another traveller called Jim. He tells me, "I'd be dead without my garden. I'm out there every day. I refuse to get help – I love it."

Edward's Garden

After breakfast I'm off up further north to the Lake District –
to visit a garden near Kendal and I know I'm going to enjoy the
scenery of the journey if nothing else. It's a glorious day and
everything feels good – even the dry stone walls look like they've
been knitted with great thick spools of wool, such is my soft focus
on the day. When I park the Daisybus up at Sprint Mill I have to
photograph her in her bright shiny yellow and white livery on
top of the delicious greens of a clover and buttercup field and
I'm singing the line 'sunshine over clover' from 'When The Roses
Come Again' by Heidi Talbot. That's a good name for the book I
think to myself.

Edward Acland describes himself as an eco-freak and he
has invented a new word 'Guardening' which he says, "means
gardening but with a serious emphasis on managing our space for
the wellbeing of **all** creatures that reside within the space, not just
ourselves." Here is a man I can identify with.

Before starting our tour of the garden that he and wife Romola
cherish, Edward first shows me an outbuilding absolutely stuffed
full of bottles and jars of preserved food. "We don't like having a
freezer as they're not environmentally friendly and we find this is
much easier for instant food anyway – you can open a jar much
quicker than you can defrost something!"

The sparklingly clear River Sprint runs through the land below
the house tumbling over rocks and boulders, shimmering over
the pebbles and I am reminded of Andrew Fusek Peters' notion
in his book **Dip** that 'a river is a lullaby in motion'. I wish Anne
Earnshaw was here with me as Edward tells me he thinks of rivers

and streams as the veins of the planet, that perhaps they're even a stream of intelligence holding the wisdom and uniqueness of our world. Edward loves the planet so much he has a problem with so called SSSIs – He thinks the whole world should be – well is – a Site of Special Scientific Interest. He says to me, "Homosapiens are the 'Guardeners' of the planet. What we do with our time here – looking after it – is such a privilege. It's a privilege to gain more and more knowledge of it and be part of the energy and power of nature."

Sitting on a tree trunk on a shingle beach by the river at the end of the garden, Edward and I lament the abuse of the planet and talk of all sorts of initiatives and hopes and promises that try to put right our negative human impact. "So often they fizzle out and are hard to sustain. There needs to be a positive contagion of new thinking. We need to follow and be led by nature rather than exploiting it," he says, and is clearly frustrated by man's wilful misuse of Earth. "Sometimes I feel quite lonely in this context."

I try to reassure him he is not alone. I think there's a new 'Cool Botanica' coming along – the emergence of a love of natural beauty and planet, a realisation that we've been cruelly exploiting our home and a refusal to give up on it. I tell him I'm meeting many people who join him in a longing for a breakthrough in human thinking and that his 'positive contagion' might be really catching.

For Edward and Romola opening their garden is a way of sharing their views as well as their land. "It's good to share with people so they can discover themselves the delight of it all and allow creative spirit to flow. Our garden promotes the wildness and wilderness within the space we love. At a recent NGS opening a visitor congratulated us on our garden, saying it was so lovely to look round a space that had clearly been handed over to God! I put my hands on my hips and said 'we do quite a lot too!' But his observation was well founded. We put handmade seats up around the space so folk can sit and just absorb the naturalness, the peacefulness and, hopefully, feel detached from the stressful outside world. At one particular point I put up a sign that says, 'Pause here and listen to the river talking.'"

"As well as the wild part we have a large vegetable and soft fruit garden, entirely organic and building in permaculture principles. We use simple hand tools, not machines, throughout. All of this is arranged in ways which I hope people find attractive and peaceful. All in all I like to feel the place has a message....avoiding meticulousness, promoting the natural, celebrating decay."

It's certainly a message that comes across loud and clear to me and reinforced by a look around the old mill itself, in which Edward exhibits his astonishing collection of 'Cagmagary' (which appears to be another word for 'stuff'). It is all beautifully and artfully displayed over the four floors of this old mill and as an extra attraction for NGS visitors it is certainly the most unusual and extraordinary I've seen. "It's my own collection of paraphernalia that has accumulated over the last forty years." he tells me.

Part of the Cagmagary are artworks Edward and his daughter Florence have made from the stuff of everyday life – rusty old used nails, bailer twine, pea pods, squashed tins from the roadside – even the gardener's dreaded couch grass – all presided over by Belinda, the 'scare-lady', who Edward describes as, "somewhat battered and tired, like Planet Earth, for being out in the cold too long. She hides away, for protection, amongst the branches, watching.... and waiting for signs of change."

With his Cagmagary Edward shows his respect for all things – inanimate as well as living, manmade as well as natural. He is a gentle, thoughtful person who, despite daily evidence to the contrary, still has an almost childlike belief in the good that might come to the world. I leave him wishing I could to help his dream

137

come true. "I'd like to think that our species can go on living on this beautiful planet as long as is literally humanly possible, ie till the sun dies, and not kill the planet before then."

Fiona's Garden

I'm off to Anglesey! I'm perhaps excessively excited about it, but it's Welsh, it's an island, it has beaches and it has gardens, so it's pretty much perfect in my view. I set off and soon leave the country piles of Shropshire behind me as I move into the Welsh countryside with its humbler, simpler dwellings, where I feel more at home.

On the way to Anglesey I'm stopping off in Denbighshire to meet an extraordinary lady, Fiona Bell. Fiona is exceptional for many reasons. One of them is that she is a gardener who sits in her garden. This is a rare skill indeed. I think I may have managed to sit for five or maybe even up to eight minutes in my garden. I'm pretty sure I've never managed ten minutes. It's called twitchy fingers syndrome – caused by critical eye disorder. The critical eye spots something that the twitchy fingers just cannot leave alone and you're off again.

But Fiona can sit for ages and today I sit with her on a bench in the garden her mother started in the 1960s and we chat and watch the birds and the hens and talk about the mystery of how gardens make us feel so good. "It's the planning as much as anything" ..... "the ideas" .... "the determination and anticipation of carrying out the plans" ..... "the joy of the results even if we'll never see them" "It's restorative – we nuture nature and nature nutures us," we variously suggest to each other.

Sitting still and enjoying your garden is something gardeners should do more often. Fiona asks me, "Are you a cat in the country or a dog in the country?" I look confused, so she explains "If you're a cat you'll just sit and watch, if you're a dog you'll tear around being endlessly busy." It can be easy for gardening to become just another form of housework and that's no fun at all. I wonder whether Fiona has gained a better perspective on the point of a garden because she has recently been quite ill with cancer. She tells me, "Being unwell for a little while has made me appreciate the garden even more, even when I return from another weekly dose of radiotherapy the sight of the spring flowers has really lifted my spirits and made me more determined to make a full recovery so that I can once again resume activities in the garden. Even thinking about it in hospital helped – people who don't garden must miss out on that – it's such a help and the minute you come home you feel instantly better."

The farmhouse is set in the Vale of Clwyd and has gorgeous views all around. Her father farmed the land in the past and the love of the land is obviously in the family's blood. Fiona tells me, "Father gave up on life when he knew he could no longer get out and engage with the land and farm. His dog lived with us after he'd died and exactly one year later he looked at me and I knew his eyes were saying 'I've had enough now' just as my father had said. At least with the dog I could do something about it. I always felt that he'd hung on just to make sure I was OK."

Farmers are well known for not caring for gardening but Fiona's mother certainly did. "She had a love of shrubs, trees and spring colour," says Fiona, "my style is quite different – I have an eye for herbaceous, herbs, wild flowers and veg but we managed to develop our respective gardens on the same farm with some sense of harmony."

After her mother died, Fiona started to make some changes. "I took down the leylandii straight away!" she says, "but the Garrya took longer – everything has a memory – a garden becomes so much more than just a plot of land with a few plants – it's all those shared moments and memories."

And it seems the family will be caring for this land for some time. With stunning barns and outbuildings ready for refurbishment and two daughters who love nature as much as she does, Fiona and Plas Ashpool have a bright future. Indeed this weekend one of her daughters is running a festival at the farm where she grew up. Having overcome her own battles with injury and illness Laura has such a zest for life and nature that she now runs ZestFest here every year – a yoga festival with food, music, nature and fun for all the family.

Because of her illness Fiona wisely decided not to open her own garden for the NGS this year but being Assistant County Organiser she is still doing her bit for the charities that have come to have more personal meaning in her life. But being an 'NGS official' doesn't make Fiona pernickety about her or other people's gardens. She shows me a half-finished garden building, now with a roof of rambling roses, the sunken rose garden is brimming with self-sown wild flowers, the hens roam freely and there are many places to sit, which is often what you will find Fiona doing –sitting and watching and loving and enjoying it. "There's no hurry" she says, "it's very much a continuation of the family – we're not going anywhere."

I leave in a calmer state than I arrived thanks to Fiona and enjoy driving slowly through the Welsh lanes on towards Anglesey. Arriving in Beaumaris I look for The Bull Hotel – apparently easy to spot in the main street of this lovely harbour town. Turns out it's easy to spot when it's not covered in scaffolding and I drive around the town three or four times before realising this. Still at least the good people of Beaumaris are in no doubt that there's a flowery yellow campervan in town promoting gardens open for charity. I anticipate a steep rise in garden visiting numbers on the island this weekend.

Ena's Garden

In her pretty little cottage – Rose Cottage – Ena Green puts my cup of tea down beside a sampler sewn with the words "A garden grows as much in the heart as in the soil" a sentiment that becomes particularly poignant as I settle down in a comfy chair looking out on to the garden and Ena bravely tells me her story.

Just five months ago Ena's husband Bryan died after a sudden and vicious cancer attack brought on by asbestos poisoning. The diagnosis came only two years into making their new garden on Anglesey and days after agreeing to open it for the NGS for the first time.

Ena courageously decided to carry on with the open day, this weekend, and with the help of friends has the garden looking so immaculate that, although I timed my visit to help with some last minute preparation, she doesn't need to put me to work today in the unseasonal drizzle. This means we can spend more time chatting – and more importantly for my part, listening. Ena really is still very much in the early days of her bereavement and I listen sadly as she tells me of the nightmare of the last few months. I remember only too well how in the early months of my own bereavement, the comfort it gave me to just have someone to talk to about the whole sad affair. I am also, today, relieved to remember that back then I didn't require anything from my listener – I didn't expect wise words or magical transformations of perception – so I feel no urge to find the 'right words' for Ena, knowing as I do that just having someone acknowledge the pain is enough for today.

Often referring back to the garden, Ena tells me she has always gardened even when her family only had a courtyard with an outside loo. She even remembers her first purchase for her own garden after leaving home – six red geraniums, some lobelia, a tub and some compost. Even as an adult she says she feels like a child 'being fetched in from playing out' when called in from the garden. Her enthusiasm has spread so that she and Bryan have also inspired friends and neighbours to start 'playing out' and even designed and made a garden at an old people's home, getting some young offenders to help with the project too.

Of course, part of the reason for continuing with the NGS open day without Bryan is to raise money for the charities – especially Marie Curie who helped her and Bryan through his last painful four days. Donations have already come in from friends and acquaintances – even from Australia where the previous owner of Ena's cottage now lives. Everyone is keen to show their support for this lady and the love she had for her husband and their joint happiness in making this garden. "Bryan was always fiddling with or fixing something," Ena smiles. "He taught himself plumbing and electrics – he could turn his hand to anything." I can see that this is how they have managed to make such a lovely garden in such a short space of time. "Sometimes I feel he is with me out there," she tells me. "Sometimes it's like my hands become his – I've done things I've never done before, like laying a path!"

At the bottom of the garden is a summerhouse where Ena keeps Bryan's memory alive with mementos of his love of steam engines. I tell her that my husband too likes a steam train and that I want to take him on one of the great steam train journeys one day. "Do it while you've got him," she says.

With a final look at the beautifully planted garden – Ena's clemmies especially make me swoon – I wish Ena all the luck in the world and reassure myself that she has plenty of help for the open day. Her new neighbours on Anglesey have rallied around and she tells me what lovely people they all are and how blessed she is to have such wonderful new friends. It is, in part, the garden that has brought this strength in numbers to her aid I think, and Ena agrees "Yes, gardening has helped me through everything."

Christine & Keith's Garden

After a sad story like Ena's, just driving past Keith and Christine Williamson's garden puts a smile on my face. In fact it makes so many drivers smile that a lot of them pull over and take photos, Keith tells me, when I stop by on my way back to meet Willy in Beaumaris. A man with a sense of humour and a bit of artistic flair, Keith doesn't do much gardening, but he does a lot of tree-clipping. He clips faces into them and the massive cypress on the roadside has the biggest of them all – a great big smiley face about twenty feet tall and six feet wide. It's mad and I love it. Keith and Christine are a friendly, modest couple who have lived on Anglesey all their lives. They say their garden is a work in progress – the huge boat in the back garden has been another and is to be launched tomorrow from Beaumaris. A fun couple, new to gardening, they both enjoy a horticultural joke where they can make one. They challenge me to find the tubers planted in the borders. I soon realise that they don't mean the flowering tubers that gardeners stick underground, but the musical tubas that they have rising out of the flowerbeds with summer bedding flowing out of the ends like music "Don't you have tubas in your garden?" Keith enquires smiling.

Some of the characters in the trees are quite ghoulish and Keith enjoys telling particularly gullible people that it used to be a graveyard and that the trees just grew like that. Christine says that they open their garden along with their neighbour who has 'a proper garden' that is described in the NGS Yellow Book as quaint and full of character. "Whereas our garden is quirky and full of characters!" she laughs.

I leave Christine and Keith to enjoy their supper and head off for mine. On the way I pass a roadside café with the sign 'Grandad's Café – Ugly Staff, Beautiful Food'.

Mike & Gill's Garden

The next day Willy comes with me to Bull Bay on Anglesey's northern coast, which on a sunny day like today is a stunning place to be, though I imagine that the rugged coastline is equally spectacular when the winter storms hit. When Mike Cross first moved to his house overlooking the bay it was some weeks before he discovered that he also owned the headland opposite and his own gully leading down to his own tiny private beach. What a lovely surprise that must have been. The difference between the headland and his back garden could not be more marked and beautifully illustrate how we can love nature and conservation at the same time as loving the man-made paradises we call gardens.

As we wander over the rough grass of the headland, Mike tells me how he was born in Kent (his mother went into labour when she was scared by a Messerschmitt!) His friends were farmers' children and he speaks nostalgically of a childhood riding on hay ricks along the main roads, catching geese, nature rambling, bird watching and fishing. After a country childhood he spent much of his life in a factory – in fact he points to the factory over the bay that he managed for much of his career. The factory extracted bromine from seawater, processing 300,000 gallons of water a minute, cleaning the sewage water that used to be pumped straight into the sea as an environmentally friendly side-effect. Keith says when the factory closed, the water became dirty again until the authorities finally put in a sewage treatment plant.

The headland still keeps its wild look but with clumps here and there of garden plants that have survived being dumped over the wall by previous occupants of nearby houses. It's a nice mix. And the birds like it too. Oystercatchers and seagulls nest here every year and they chase off any newcomers like the heron that tried to move in recently. Mike has placed seating made from recycled materials in the best positions for views across the bay and out to the Irish Sea. Like Edward Acland back in Cumbria, Mike is passionate about the future of the planet and warns me of his certainty of an upcoming Ice Age, which confuses me as at the moment we are more worried about melting ice caps than freezing oceans. Further interesting apparent paradoxes pop up in conversation as we talk about the usefulness of nuclear power. Traditional eco-warriors are mostly anti-nuclear but if we are to stop using fossil fuels perhaps we need to look again at our established convictions and examine our real options.

I am reminded at this point of Monty Don's Radio 4 programme **Shared Planet** which looks at the problems caused by the needs of human life on a planet shared with other life forms. It doesn't have the answers but it is such a good programme for realising what the questions are. Of course, Monty Don has written much on gardening too – not least about how his connection with nature helps him with his depression. He is another of my gardening heroes.

Moving from the wild and natural headland across the coastal road to Mike's house we meet his partner, Gill Boniface, in their amazing densely planted, colourful and decorative back garden. Gill brings tea to the top of the garden for us all to share and while Mike shows Willy around the cleverly designed borders, Gill tells me how she came to be living here with Mike after a divorce and a breakdown severely disrupted her life. "Gardening saved my life, brought me back into the world," she says. "It was my saviour".

But Gill had to prove herself worthy of Mike's garden when she arrived. "He wouldn't let me touch anything at first," she laughs. "He was very protective of the garden and I had to work hard to gain his trust!" But after allowing her a little patch here and there to play with he soon realised he had an excellent plantswoman with a good eye for design and detail on board. Their mutual love of plants and nature has made this garden into one of the most impressive I've seen. "We spend lots of time visiting and enjoying gardens all over the country" Gill tells me, "and we have to continually make room for new plants we want to grow – our lawn is getting smaller and smaller!"

The couple used to enter local gardening competitions but after winning for several years on the trot they decided to withdraw because they didn't want to discourage other people from having a go!

But they still love to inspire others, including their neighbours, who have recently started gardening. Gill tells me, "One visitor recently said thoughtfully as she left 'I'm going back to have a re-think!'" and I can see why. Gill and Mike have used their available space so cleverly and proved you don't need acres to create a garden full of character and packed full of plants. "Sharing this passion, which gives us so much and such a feeling of wellbeing, has become a major part of our life. The NGS allows us to share this with other people while supporting some vital charities."

And that, in a nutshell, is what it's all about at the end of the day – they're a caring lot, the NGS Garden Owners.

Jenny's Garden

Across the Menai Straits back in North Wales, Jenny and Brian Osborne know a thing or two about caring. I have not heard it before, but their story and the story of their daughter Becky has featured in many newspaper and magazine articles over the years and their garden has won awards and even been photographed by Lord Lichfield.

But this is not a grand garden, not a formal garden, in fact it is not like any garden I have ever seen before. Meeting Jenny and Brian at their old mill house turns out to be a highlight of my tour. Brian will take no personal praise for the garden at all, though it turns out he has in fact built the many bridges and steps that lead you around this wonderland, not to mention rescuing the condemned house nestled under a bridge by the river and turning it into their quirky home. It was Brian who invited me to Foxbrush Garden, telling me in a letter of how their story goes back to when the couple had two severely handicapped girls who they cared for and educated at home. "Except I could 'escape' to work and Jenny found turning this old mill wilderness into a garden her 'release', even though it was in quick ten minute stints" he wrote. "Today she still gardens, on her own, as it is truly HER garden."

Jenny made the garden by stepping outside her back door and simply digging and planting. And doing that for 33 years. Sometimes it was to relieve frustration, other times to grab a few moments of peace and a lot of time was spent enjoying gardening with her daughter Becky by her side. There was no grand design and walking around with gentle Jenny today I can easily imagine her just stepping out, clearing a patch, planting whatever came cheaply to hand, allowing the prettier weeds to fill the gaps and simply continuing until, well, until today. And she will more than likely continue tomorrow.

Brian and Jenny's first daughter Vicky was severely handicapped and died aged five – a hard enough blow for one life, but the couple had another two girls, one mercifully healthy and another handicapped daughter, Becky. Becky was an extraordinary girl who developed her own passion for gardening and who, given her circumstances, specialised in miniature gardening with alpine plants in containers made by her father, wheelbarrows and boxes. Her creations were so good they featured on television and in magazines and her flair led to awards and accolades from many quarters. Becky also had a talent for writing and wrote for the Alpine Garden Society as well as writing novels. The paths Brian made at Foxbrush were always wheelchair-wide and in this way Becky was able to be a real help and companion to Jenny in the garden. The three of them also used to take part in Sealed Knot events and in their little Millers Cottage in the garden, set as it would have been when a family once lived there, you can see the beautifully stitched costumes Jenny made. The loss of her daughter and gardening companion when Becky was just 28 is too heartrending. Needless to say Jenny found it difficult to return to the garden for some time.

My visit to Foxbrush was heartbreakingly beautiful. The location, the people, the garden, the nature, seeped into my soul and will live there for ever.

Anthony's Garden

I remember Yvonne's expression 'gardening as an extreme sport' when Anthony Taverner shows me around Plas Cadnant on Anglesey. Anthony is not doing anything by halves. The house at Plas Cadnant was derelict and the grounds overgrown when he arrived in 1996 but they are now exquisitely restored and maintained. "It's all my hobbies rolled into one," he tells me: "History, landscape, architecture and gardening". It is an extraordinary achievement because Anthony has not just restored the original gardens around the house, but he has reshaped the grounds in the very grand 'Victorian Picturesque' style. I'm not aware of anyone else doing such grand landscaping these days – it's certainly rare to see a private garden being created on this scale. It's the sort of thing that was being done by rich landowners in the 19th century – the sort of place the National Trust and Tim Smit would 'rediscover'. But this is all new. For a private garden it is quite an amazing undertaking (and, I imagine, horrendously expensive).

The valley gardens with belvederes, rocky outcrops, waterfalls and woodland walks have all been skilfully designed and created by Anthony who says he is influenced somewhat by the writing and planting of Gertrude Jekyll and Humphrey Repton of the picturesque. He is not a trained horticulturalist but a farmer from Staffordshire, whose family expectations did not include training at Kew, which is what Anthony had always wanted to do. But boy is he making up for it now! His plant knowledge is impressive – naming each and every plant that we pass, some of which I have never seen before. He enjoys unusual specimens like the 'freefall box', 'fishtail camellias', hardy echiums and hundreds of ferns. He tells me he wants to improve on the Victorian gardens by ensuring that the structures – specially chosen rocks and beautifully carved waterfalls and streams – are not ultimately lost behind fully grown plants, so the planting is lush but restrained to appropriately sized plants that will not overpower and ruin the design. He's using plenty of alpines planted at eye level above the paths, which are works of art in their own right. It is all so incredibly tasteful! And not for the first or last time I say to myself "How dare you call yourself a gardener?! You're such a clumsy amateur!"

As well as opening for the NGS Anthony is welcoming the public to his holiday cottages in some beautifully restored old buildings. "Having laboured away to restore the place, I want it to be sustainable in the future, so now I open it to the public and the income generated helps with the upkeep." As we walk back across the immaculate lawn, he calls to his gardener that he spotted a nettle in the woods. A nettle – one nettle! I cringe inwardly at the thought of Anthony visiting my garden and as the master and gardener head off to deal with one nettle and perhaps a rogue dandelion, I determine that I will never invite him.

Again and again on this trip I feel embarrassed at my own inadequacy as a gardener, especially as I appear to be representing the NGS with its logo all over the Daisybus and having their support to do this thing. At the first sign of any deference towards my greater knowledge I soon put people right and declare myself to be the shambolic beginner that I am and if I am helping them in their garden I ask for precise instructions, especially on the matter of weeds. It has always been said that one man's weeds are another's wild flowers so I could easily have spent an afternoon totally wrecking someone's wildflower patch in an attempt to be helpful. Though to be honest I am more likely to be criticised for not removing weeds than destroying them as Willy and I enjoy things

Caroline and David in Wilmslow

Smiling Tree on Anglesey

Lavinia's Lurking Lady

Me with Sue Beck in her day lily garden

The Team at Rhubarb Farm

We agree!

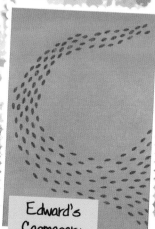

Edward's Cagmagary

like willowherb and hedge mustard and coltsfoot in our garden and positively encourage ground covers like wild strawberries and yellow archangel.

I have begun to think of this trip as a kind of apprenticeship. I learn something new from each of the gardens I visit – a new plant, a new trick, a new way of doing something, a new specialist nursery. By the end of the year I should have enough knowledge to make the very best garden in the country – at least in my imagination.

Julian's Garden

It's 20th June and I feel intrepid – I'm going to the top of the Sychnant Pass. You have to be an intrepid traveller to climb a pass. Even if it's very slowly in an ancient campervan. Intrepid travellers are always rewarded with incredible views, along with their frostbite and vertigo, and I am happy to accept my reward as we turn into Pensychnant Conservation Centre, looking back on the spectacular scenery of the North Wales hills and coast. It's the sort of scene that makes you love the earth and want to care for it. It's like the 'Overview Effect' – the feeling astronauts get when they look back at little old planet earth – a strong feeling that we must unite as a race to protect this beautiful, fragile place.

And the people I'm meeting here are certainly doing their bit for this little piece of the earth and following the tradition started by Brian Henthorn Stott, descendant of the rich cotton mill family who built their house here. His love of nature and this place in particular led to the setting up of the Pensychnant Foundation 'to protect the history and natural history for peaceful enjoyment for posterity'.

Head Gardener Anne, just back from her holidays, welcomes me with coffee and biscuits and tells me that Julian, the warden, is on the beach organising a Beach Clean but may be back soon as it is raining. We both agree the turnout of help may not be as overwhelming as it might be on a lovely day.

I enjoy my drink out of the rain and ponder whether I like this strange house I'm sitting in or not. It could either be very prettily arts and crafts or spookily gothic. It probably depends on the weather I decide. It certainly needs some repairs but finances are tight for the Foundation which sticks firmly to wishes of Mr Stott working with naturalists and wildlife projects at a local level, hosting lectures and exhibitions and providing a venue for many clubs and societies involved with appreciation and preservation of nature. My suggestions that the outbuildings would make fabulous holiday lets and bring in some money seems crass when Julian answers gently that this isn't what Pensychnant is about – it's all about nature here and anything that might disturb that isn't an option. Still they do a lot of other stuff that brings people in with bird watching and botanical walks, moth nights and gardening days and happily welcome anyone interested in the natural world.

Julian tells me that they're not aiming to be world leaders in conservation but simply to honour the place and share it with others who might, they hope, leave with a renewed appreciation of nature. It's this small-scale nurturing that we can all do in our own way and if we can all care for a fraction of the whole of this earth then the whole might survive. As we roll back down the hill devouring the view we agree with the astronauts – She is so beautiful. We must save her.

Karen & Malcolm's Garden

I continue notionally hugging the hills all the way back home from North Wales and very soon we're back in the Marches countryside again, my familiar border country. My next visit is such a short distance away that I can visit on my way to a party in entirely unsuitable shoes. Pant Hall has recently changed owners from one seasoned gardener to two new ones fresh in from London and leaping hands and feet first into the hard work and joy of creating something very special here together.

"Our personal stories written on the land" is how Karen, rather beautifully, describes their venture. Karen has a way with words and both she and her partner Malcolm are creative sorts who are relishing the chance to make this natural artwork together, incorporating symbolism of important elements of their lives. I am glad I live nearby because I can't wait to see this garden in a few years' time with its new cloister garden, terraced paths below three acres of newly planted woodland (very hard work) and most excitingly, a dance floor and band stand for the expression of their love of country music and dancing. Malcolm says parts of the garden are inspired by Southend-on-Sea where he grew up, though I can't see it myself and I wonder whether he is teasing me. But then I don't really know Southend-on-Sea - maybe it does have bits that look like the Welsh Marches.....

As I totter around the garden in my party shoes Karen tells me that they opened the garden for the first time the summer they arrived because, although they knew they were going to be changing a lot, they wanted the previous owner who had always been too modest and shy to offer her garden to the NGS, to come along and accept the accolades after years of creating her lovely valley paradise.

And the couple are lucky indeed to have inherited a very pretty garden that drops down the hill away from the house. On the one side they have an established garden and on the other they are creating their own masterpiece. As they say, "It's a mix of history, mystery, present and future – Nature, nuture, romance – The wild, the whimsical and the formal – Fun, fancy and silence." I imagine Karen will be writing as much as planting over the next few years – like me feeling the urge to honour the land and the love, the biophilia, very much in evidence here in the borders.

Susie's Garden

Honouring the place is something Willy and I consider of the highest importance when gardening, but that is because we have been lucky to make a garden in a very rural natural setting. If you're making a garden in a town or very suburban setting, perhaps a small square fenced garden, then I reckon you can do pretty much what you want – make it a tropical garden, a gravel garden, a parterre, a courtyard, whatever takes your fancy. But when surrounded by 'natural' countryside some things seem more right than others. Sometimes this natural countryside has been shaped by centuries of farming and hunting and sometimes acres and acres of it have been in the same family's hands, which brings with it another type of duty – honouring your ancestors.

Susie Robinson invited me to Moorwood near Cirencester. As usual on this journey I have no idea what sort of place Moorwood is when I set off but I have been intrigued by her description of their "established romantic garden which we have 'ungardened' to go wilder to suit its Cotswold valley setting and our national collection of rambler roses."

So as we're driving over I'm thinking of a pretty Cotswold stone house and a large cottage garden perhaps, and am thrown into a state of anxiety when I start driving up to a large country mansion. I feel underdressed and even more nervous when Susie says the Princess Royal was there yesterday. Thank goodness that was yesterday methinks and thank goodness I have Willy with me today who can talk posh (he knows the secret code) while I just moon around saying "Oh what lovely roses".

Despite its grand house, I find the garden is instantly a relaxing and peaceful place to be. Roses are scrambling, clambering and rambling everywhere. Susie says, "It's really just happy chance that we have the national collection of rambler roses – perhaps because no-one else had room for it!" she laughs.

When Susie and her husband took over Moor Wood from his parents, the old gardener could no longer cope. Employing full time gardeners to maintain a large country house garden wasn't an option – or even particularly desirable. "It was an opportunity to go wilder," Susie tells me. A garden designer friend advised on removing the large herbaceous borders and playing with the perspective – drawing in the land surrounding the garden. They took the plunge and it works beautifully.

I love this feel of a garden in graceful retirement. Herbaceous borders here now would feel so fussy and overdone – an artificial nonsense compared to the serenity that the place radiates. With the walls of Cotswold stone of the house and garden covered with roses it almost has the look of an abandoned garden and Susie tells me most of the ramblers are left unpruned to do what they will. Some cascade over walls, other scramble up trees or up banks into bushes.

Susie loves the trees and especially her apple trees in the old kitchen garden. Having the same land in the same family for hundreds of years means little changes and that is great for nature. Knowing that the family will be living there for the foreseeable future means these people really are planting for future generations. But Susie says it's not all about the descendants. "When planting a tree you make an indelible mark on the landscape." I wonder if this is what all us gardeners are doing? Is it all about achieving some sort of immortality? Trees are perhaps the "I woz 'ere" graffiti of gardeners.

Susie tells me how they think thirty years ahead with their tree planting and we talk more about how the once labour intensive garden becomes more natural and wild as the years go by and it suddenly comes as some surprise to me to realise that these aristocratic families are in fact some of our best conservationists. The gentry, inheriting the sort of huge acreage and grand gardens that first opened for the NGS, are by necessity having to 'ungarden' as Susie calls it, thereby creating and preserving wonderful new habitats for all. Of course, this is something the National Trust is doing on behalf of many an ancient family who could no longer afford to run those incredibly expensive houses and gardens – and many of us Joe Public are gardening with wildlife in mind too, like my friend Karen at Hopton House in Shropshire who gets great pleasure – and fabulous photographs of wildlife – from her garden without particularly being 'A Gardener'. It had not occurred to me until today that there must be many medium and smaller country estates where people are doing the same thing in private and creating fabulous habitats almost by default.

Being back in the Cotswolds still feels like coming home and we drive along lanes beside fields of wheat, so different to the sheep, orchard and hop country we now live in. We remember with fondness the larks that used to fly above the field outside our house in Taston. Suddenly I miss the larks so much I could cry but this is silly nostalgia because our home in Worcestershire has a zillion more birds than we had in Oxfordshire.

Sue's Garden

On the morning I set off for Sue Beck's house in Cirencester a thrush on top of the robinia tree is belting out various hits from its repertoire. They make me laugh the thrushes – it's like they can't decide which tune to sing, always flicking through the playlist. They remind me of the fairy lights at Christmas that have different settings – I am thrush-like in my indecision and keep changing the display.

Sue Beck must be one of the NGS's favourite people, having with her husband John, opened their garden for the past 36 years. I decide it would be rude to ask how much they've raised in that time but it will be quite a lot and I soon learn that helping others has been an inherent part of their lives and that the nursing charities that benefit from the garden openings are close to their hearts having lost both John's mother and Sue's father to cancer.

As John was a vicar, their first house belonged to the church, and the garden they made there features in the book *The English Vicarage Garden*. But since John retired they have moved to a smaller garden, still in Cirencester, and still, by the looks of things with the same number of plants. Sue tells me how they carried their favourite plants in the paniers of their bicycles from one house to the other when they moved. Living in town they don't have a car, which also explained why I had to park the Daisybus in a neighbour's drive. Their driveway, and indeed the use of their front door, have long since disappeared and been transformed into a welcoming paradise of rose arches, clematis obelisks and the beginnings of the incredible collection of day lillies that continues around the side alley. Here, plants queue for a space in the garden like pretty ladies outside the loos at Chelsea. Sue's passion for hemerocallis has won her a medal for services to the Hosta and Hemerocallis Society. But I haven't seen anything yet....

"Wow!" I say, as I come through into the back garden – and it really is a 'Wow Garden'. Again I am amazed at how people with small gardens use their space so cleverly. This garden looks as if it goes on for ever, the planting so dense that I am completely unaware of the boundaries. And it's such a joyful place – the plants bounce and sway in the breeze, all of them looking utterly healthy and happy.

Half-hidden in the borders is a friend, also John, who has come to give Sue a hand today. They share a love of plants, cathedrals and Mozart – sometimes they play Mozart while they're in the garden. I think I'm going to enjoy my afternoon helping here. But first, Sue has prepared a beautiful lunch and we three sit in her summerhouse and we're joined by Norman the County Organiser for the Gloucestershire NGS. He's here to take photographs of the garden and the Daisybus for the local press.

Sue tells us all about her life as a vicar's wife and it seems to me the church got two for the price of one with Sue and John given the commitment and involvement Sue happily gave them, even giving up her job at Whitbreads to help full-time. When John was appointed Assistant Priest and Organ Scholar at Cheltenham Cathedral he was in charge of the choir and Sue helped organise twenty three concerts including one they were particularly proud to arrange featuring Simon Preston, the organist from Westminster Abbey. I ask Sue if as a vicar's wife she found people turning to her in times of need but she is modest in reply although she does tells me she remembers being like a second mother to the choristers who would run to her when things weren't going so well.

Again I see that for this couple Love is a guiding force in their lives and indeed Sue says the garden might be summed up in the phrase Faith, Hope and Love. She tells me, "Love incorporates our love of plants, creation and also the hope that we can pass this on to visitors, so that they can enjoy them too in their own gardens. Plus, by their generosity in paying to see the garden, visitors are showing love in donating to the good causes supported by the NGS."

I do indeed spend a happy afternoon helping in the garden removing the dead leaves from the day lillies. It seems this could be a full time job itself and frankly one I would be perfectly happy to take on. Crouching down, becoming part of the borders myself, I jostle with grasses planted as companions and get intimate with geraniums taking their chances here and there and verbascums popping up through the foliage. It is a joyful garden and though I am in a residential area of a town I could be a million miles deep in a universe of flowers such is the paradisiacal feeling here – helped I'm sure by the nourishment of love.

Rhubarb Farm

My next stop is an exciting place on the Nottinghamshire/ Derbyshire border. Unusually for me, I am a little early so I turn into Dukeries Antiques Centre when I see they have a café to find a little breakfast. I got lucky here because they have the loveliest courtyard for their tearoom with the tables amongst the outdoor antiques and greenery. At first I am not sure whether the greenery just happens to be there but on closer inspection over my tea and toast I decide someone knows exactly what they are doing here. With my Sherlock hat on I deduce that the ivies climbing over the walls and statues are unusual varieties and the lack of nettles and docks mean indubitably that this disguise is fiendishly and cleverly premeditated. Dr Watson might think that this is a neglected and abandoned spot but they're not fooling me. I love this look of mystery and romance and long to buy almost everything in front of me, but settle for another round of toast instead before I set off for Rhubarb Farm. Along with TWIGS in Swindon, this social enterprise is making a big difference to a lot of people's lives. It is another wonderfully positive gardening project and I can't wait to look around.

Jennie Street welcomes me – it's a hot July day and first she shows me around the office, a converted shipping container, which has thankfully been adapted so that we're not all cooking inside. I am introduced to the office staff, a happy mix of folk who have come to be working here with a range of issues and needs.

"Different organisations refer to us – Sam, for example, is our training assistant and was referred to us by an organisation called Help to Work. She was 23 and had severe agoraphobia" Jennie tells me, "She couldn't leave the house and never thought she'd do anything. She had no GCSEs, no confidence whatsoever and didn't see a future for herself. They had to accompany her on a bus, because she couldn't do it herself. She didn't want to see anyone or talk to anyone, in fact. She didn't want to be here at all and would only work with Lesley in corners of the field. But she was very good at IT and over 18 months here she blossomed. We employed her last November as Training Assistant and then she got another job as an admin assistant. Yesterday I went to an event where she was organising and walking around talking to people." Jennie and I beam with delight at this success story.

Introducing me, Jennie says, "This is Julie, our Training Officer. Employing her enabled us to employ Sam as well, as she could guide Sam."

"We have Anna here who also came as a client, to help her with her MS, when as a young woman in her 30s she became ill and all the official authorities could offer was a day-centre slot."

Now Anna is a Rhubarb Farm volunteer and she also employs another Rhubarb Farm volunteer, Megan, as her carer. Jennie continues, "She's in a wheelchair with MS but that has not stopped her being economically and socially productive. Before, she was just sat at home and all the social worker said was 'I can get you into a day centre', which isn't what she wants at 37. She was a rock climber, an outdoor sports tutor and a gardener trained in horticulture but got sacked as soon as her employer found out she had MS."

"Now she is also a Rhubarb Farm Ambassador and supports Philip, who is excluded from school, helping him with his literacy."

"We've got two Polish people here – there's a lot of hostility towards Polish people round here and their being here is helping to break down barriers. Everybody who comes helps breaks down barriers and stereotypes."

Outside I meet Debbie, the Volunteer Co-ordinator. Jennie says: "Debbie first came when I did a vegetable-growing course – she was a social worker with Derbyshire County Council in Family Intensive Support, working with troubled families, and her manager let her teach our cookery courses because it tied up with the families she was working with. Then when the job came up here she was just the right person."

Debbie is working with a young lad weeding a vegetable bed, "We've got two kids here today from different schools," explains Jenny. "They come to us on what's called Independent Alternative Placements. Sean was going to be excluded from school. We had to go to a meeting as advocates for him and they placed him with us for three full weeks."

Things don't always run smoothly at first. Jennie says, "First time round the taxi driver dropped him down in the village because he'd persuaded him he could walk up and he went off to his girlfriend's instead!"

"We also get referrals from the Job Centre – people who are not on a work programme but need to be moved forward."

"We have prisoners from an open prison here too. The local authority were initially worried about mixing school students and prisoners and people with drug and alcohol problems, but it works perfectly – there's no issues at all. The reason is I think because everybody who comes a) is treated with value and without judgement and b) most people who come here want to do something with their lives and when they see other people wanting to do something too, it's the opposite of a downward spiral – there's a positive, ripple in the pond effect."

Pointing down the site Jennie says, "There's a prisoner repairing our compost toilet roof today. We had a 17 year old who killed someone driving. He was very depressed but went away more positive. And there's another guy who we are now thinking of doing a big partnership with, growing trees because he grows thousands of trees. He came to us from the court and he says Rhubarb Farm kept him above ground. His mental health had deteriorated so much when he was convicted, but he now runs his own business. He's working with a French company and he's already planted 1,600 trees with them."

"We've set a project up for the prisoners: if any of them can't or don't want to go back to where they come from because of their crime – usually they're lifers at the end of their sentences, we'll help them get re-housed here under a system called the Integrated Offender Management Scheme. I just had a conversation with one such man this morning because he's been expressing an interest to come and live here. We will support him through the transition. He'll just be part of the team."

A fit, tanned young man approaches. "Luke is one of our staff," Jennie introduces him. "He first came to us on day release from prison."

Luke says, "I did a lot of years in prison and I got a lot of qualifications – maths and English diplomas, railway engineering, forklift – to better myself. I was against volunteering to start with cos I didn't get paid for it, but it rewarded me in other ways. I now work with prisoners who are on day release. It's where I wanted to go in life. I'm not an office worker!"

Luke and the other prisoners are working in a large field that six weeks ago was covered in brambles and weeds – just four of them have turned it into a well-organised-vegetable-growing site in just six weeks.

"We wash and clean and bundle the veg before it goes up for the veg boxes that go out from here," says Luke. He tells me his own kids love gardening too. Working at Rhubarb Farm has helped him learn about autism and how to cope with his son who is autistic.

Jennie has enormous energy and dedication and spends a lot of time getting support for the Farm – financial and otherwise. I wonder whether it must seem like an uphill struggle at times. She tells me, "It's difficult to be self-sustaining in horticulture so we get grants and have some contracts with local authorities and schools. We won a Big Lottery award of nearly a quarter of a million pounds for a five-year project to get mental health sufferers back into work."

"We also won a national award to expand the work on Luke's field to generate more income for the Farm. When you grow for therapeutic reasons you suffer a loss because people don't know how to sow seeds or transplant. They plant too deep or too shallow, plants get hoed that shouldn't or they aren't watered enough. So the grant to helps us become more commercial."

We meet Tom and Philip weeding around the cauliflowers and Jennie shows Tom an easier way to turn the soil. Philip has just gained his Land-Based Training qualification.

Jennie says, "We're really pleased. It's marvellous – you've done really well. What do your teachers say?"

"They don't know," says Philip

"You've got to tell them!" says Jennie and Philip grins. I ask him if he wants to carry on gardening.

"Yes I'm also doing catering," he answers

"Great – so are you going to bring the two together then? Growing it then cooking it? You'll be on Masterchef next!"

There is a fun atmosphere here and Jennie says it's important that everyone is open and honest with each other. I find that I am so relaxed that when I meet a prisoner on day release for criminal damage say "Keep away from my bus then," before I can stop myself. Thankfully they all laugh and Jennie says, "That's the right thing to say here!" Another of the prisoners offers to fix my broken windscreen wiper and he does this while my tour continues.

"We have Corporate Days here too – this pond was dug by Sainsbury's. It's good team-building – people love it." Next to the pond is a lovely building that looks a bit like a bandstand. "Chesterfield College construction students built this – they were taught how to do different types of brickwork which is why it looks so decorative. The firepit was put in for our environmental after school club."

We go for lunch together in the Mess Room. Jennie has made a rhubarb fool especially for me as I had cheekily asked whether there would be any when I visited. It is delicious and we talk several of the lads who have never eaten rhubarb before into trying it. They all admit they like it. Before they go back to work and I head off we take photographs of our yellow busses together and make silly jokes about what might happen if we put them in a garage together. I leave a place full of happy, positive people and I am so glad for Jennie's energy and dedication and I am glad too, that it is all paying off. So many broken lives mended and renewed.

Caroline's Garden

I'm on the road again up to Cheshire and Lancashire. So much of this year is being spent on the road, lots of it on boring motorways and by-passes, but some nice sight-seeing pootles too. Being blown across lanes on the motorways: not good. Climbing slowly up hills with time to appreciate the views: great. The bigger the hill, the more opportunity to take in the view, change the music, check my email, polish my nails. Sometimes the hills are so steep I wonder if it is actually feasible for a VW camper to get up them at all. But so far, so good.

And so to Wilmslow in Cheshire to meet Caroline Meliar-Smith – an actress, teacher and social worker who tells me her garden is her therapist, her stress buster: "It accepts me in whatever frame of mind I am in, in all seasons, without question. The garden cares for me as I care for it".

As vivacious as you would expect an actress to be, Caroline is a fun person to be around and the morning I spend with her, her husband David and a local journalist is full of sunshine and laughs.

"I originally trained as an actor, but my parents only paid for the course on the understanding that I would then go on to train as a teacher," Caroline tells me. "I became a Primary/Secondary teacher and married David. We went to Australia for 6 years and had 2 children. In Australia I worked with a social worker doing therapeutic life mapping with school children. On our return to the UK, I retrained as a Social worker, keeping up the drama in Community Theatre which was by now a valuable therapy counteracting the stress of Social Work. At this time, we moved to our present home and returned to gardening as a stress buster."

168

"When I retired, I moved back into professional acting and in the first 3 years I met up with Monty Don on the set of a film called **'Grow your Own'** directed by Richard Laxton. The film deals with therapeutic healing experienced by Chinese refugees working on an allotment in Liverpool. I had a small role, and was able to talk to Monty regarding his strong belief in the healing power of horticulture. Many of the actors in that film also used gardening to relieve stress."

Caroline has always been aware of the therapeutic nature of gardens. As a child her mother always told her to leave her father alone in the garden after a hard day's work and, throughout her adult life, Caroline has used gardening as a basis for healing.

"My drama training came to the fore when I ran Role Play Training & Drama Therapy for staff and patients at St. Ann's Hospice, Manchester. While working as Bereavement Manager in the Hospice I recognised patients trying to come to terms with their losses, including, in some cases loss of their gardens. I helped to bring in a greenhouse to encourage simple garden therapy."

Caroline is still an Actor, still promoting the therapeutic values of both acting and gardening. A trained Public Speaker, she does three talks; one of which promotes the joys, health and healing a garden can bring to everyone – crossing all age, gender and cultural boundaries. "This is what we both love to share when we open our garden each year," she tells me.

Reflecting on what Caroline told me as I drove home, I realised that the grief of leaving a garden was something I had not thought about before and something that makes me hope, if I ever find myself in a hospice, it will be one with a garden.

Near my home in Herefordshire, we have a hospice where they give as much thought to the external environment as the internal. Garden Designer Hannah Genders has made a special garden for St Michael's Hospice which reflects the path of life. The hospice also has strong links with nature and gardens through The Hellens Garden Festival, devoted to the love of plants and planet. The festival happens every year in June, and is, I think, one of the nicest, friendliest festivals I attend.

This is also a good time to mention one of my favourite charities – Greenfingers. This is a wonderful organisation that makes gardens for children's hospices. Often the children can't be outside for very long so it is important that there are gardens right there on site, allowing them to get as much fresh air, sunshine and enjoyment out of nature as possible. The gardens also provide somewhere for families to picnic together and share some precious moments.

Jill Smith, a member of our Hortihub in Herefordshire and part of the Quiet Garden Movement, has another perspective too. Having worked as a hospice chaplain for many years she tells me, "It's a great privilege to walk with people and their families and to take their funerals and hold remembering services, but in this position grief creeps up and in you quietly for all those you have held and walked with. I have always gardened so I suppose I just went to the garden again in my grief to allow God to heal, refresh and speak to me. And he did and continues to do so. That's why I do Quiet Garden and NGS – to share our plot. Nothing is more pleasing than finding someone asleep or just being. On those days it means the garden is speaking to them and their needs."

Ultimately these links with nature when facing death are all about accepting the cycle of life and coming to believe in renewal, even reincarnation in one form or another. All life is energy and energy is impossible to destroy.

Next, a loathsome journey being buffeted by lorries up the M6 takes me to the Royal Umpire Caravan Park near Southport. On arrival the first thing I notice on the way in is that there is a Wyevale right next door.

I have met several people who swear by their Parking Fairy – as they drive towards a destination they ask their Parking Fairy for a space exactly where they want it. Apparently it never fails. It's all about positive thinking so I thought I'd try it. But rather than a Parking Fairy I create myself a Wyevale Fairy. Driving long distances, I pass lots of places to stop and eat but nowhere makes me feel more at home than a garden centre. After hours on the road I'm feeling tired and hungry and green-deficient, so I start praying for a Wyevale Garden Centre sign. And, unbelievably, it worked! Jumping down from the Daisybus I stagger through the entrance and walk slowly, only partly due to stiffness, through the welcoming and enticing display of young plants looking their very best. For me it is a joy to be in the company of plants again and I linger among the scents and feels of these beautiful green treasures. I am instantly calmed.

After a cold and uncomfortable night in the Daisybus it's bliss to have breakfast here, not least because of the comfort of their clean, warm loos. The folk are nice too – arriving early in the morning I'm often the first in the café and feel part of the gang as the staff prepare for their day; in Leicestershire I am asked to help remember the names of the three musketeers; in Derbyshire I'm encouraged to have as much as I want for breakfast even if it does look greedy; in Lincolnshire a kind waitress alerts me that I have tucked my skirt into my knickers. I like to be alone for long periods, but contact with people feels good after a bad night and I am reminded that people do need other people. Perhaps that's why gardeners, who often work alone, are so friendly when they come together. It also explains why community gardening projects give so much more than an opportunity for exercise to those taking part.

The Royal Umpire Caravan Park seems to be an intergalactic landing station because the 'caravans' there are the most enormous things I've ever seen – I didn't know you could actually get caravans that big. They could, to me, quite easily have come via Mars. Making my way, jaw dropping, past the spacevans, in the morning I set off to meet Lavinia Tod at her home in Ramsbottom.

Lavinia's Garden

Sadly Lavinia is no stranger to bereavement but she is another lady with the strength, sense of humour, courage and creative talent to carry on.

When her partner died suddenly the shock was huge. With both parents still alive she had never experienced such loss and truly thought she couldn't cope. As depression set in she found her garden helped her at least physically: "Digging 'til I dropped enabled me to get some sleep," she tells me. Then a visit to Plas Newydd and inspiration from Rex Whistler's famous painting inspired her to take up painting again. Using the biggest canvasses she could find, Lavinia started in earnest – beginning in the morning and painting all day without even stopping to eat.

An impressed friend got Lavinia's art into a gallery but Lavinia went incognito to the exhibition, still preferring to keep a quiet life. Then a car crash stopped her painting and she started back in the garden. "I seem to get jolted in and out of things!" she says.

We're sitting in the garden of her house – one of several built on the site of a former church. It is beautifully planted with many quirky, clever and funny embellishments, but it is small and Lavinia's creative urge is large. So she started to borrow the churchyard – first putting some old wheels in the fence to make round windows to look through, then putting in a pretty lych-gate so she could walk through. Then, through her wheel windows, she noticed some daffodils under a tree and decided she would bulk them up a bit. Then "just popped" a few plants in that were going spare….. Yes, Lavinia had become a Guerilla Gardener!

There is something truly wonderful about guerrilla gardening –

bits of neglected land becoming beautiful with the simple fly-by-night detonation of a seed bomb or with the regular kind attention of someone local who decides to love a bit of land no-one else is loving. I can almost feel the gratitude of those buried in Lavinia's churchyard.

Now her parents' ashes are here too. Another unhappy period has passed, in which her father died and then her mother too, via a long, heart-breaking struggle with dementia and care homes. Lavinia, now with new partner Brad, is again picking up the pieces and keeping on keeping on.

But, as usual, with folk who have been through so much, the talk is not all sad. In fact it turns out to be one of my most educational visits. Both Lavinia and Brad have a great interest in history and our conversation about gardens, death and healing is interspersed with interesting snippets of local history. The past, the present and the future all seem to be making a lot of sense in this garden-cum-churchyard.

Lavinia is well known in the locality for her gardening and people leave unwanted plants by her gate for her to plant. It is important to her that other people do come and enjoy the churchyard – she isn't being acquisitive about it. She's naturally a very generous lady and wants to show me two other gardens that her neighbours have made while I am there. Walking down the road towards friend David's house (an incredibly impressive and neat garden) she points to the verge on the other side where Brad is cutting the grass around some wild flowers "That's our latest project!" Lavinia smiles, and I think how lucky folk round here are to have her spreading her love of plants all around.

Again, contemplating the love and loss in my own life on my drive home, I wonder how people with no easy access to green spaces cope with bereavement. Hopefully they will at the very least have a nice graveyard to visit.

Arriving back home I see my regale lilies have burst open and joined the roses along the front path for the summer crescendo. I feel like a bride (albeit in my dirty travelling clothes) walking down a ceremonial archway of exquisite scent and beauty. And then I am flattened by a quivering, whimpering ecstatic Daisydog.

Beverley Allotments

I cross the Humber Bridge! It feels like a rite of passage – epic, like I've truly travelled and am now a fully qualified citizen of the UK. I can now legitimately call myself properly British. I can't explain it but that's how it feels.

Unusually for me, I arrive early at Beverley Allotments and a nice lady called Margaret lets me in the small gate off the main road. I am immediately out of the busyness of the city and into heaven. I drive slowly, like a queen, down the middle of the allotments. At either side of me many different renditions of the joy of gardening stand to attention. In the distance, the Minster rises, shining above the city, which, from my location, appears to be bathed in sunlight and flowers and full of cheerful people. I stop the Daisybus two or three times to jump out and photograph her next to an especially lovely plot until I realise they are all photo-worthy and decide it's time to meet the people instead.

Howard is the first to say a merry good morning and we have barely introduced ourselves before he has thrust a punnet of raspberries into my hand and invited me to dig up some of his potatoes. Why is it that you never get over the excitement of digging up potatoes – turning over the soil to discover golden, edible nuggets. Howard says his allotment is his gym – "It keeps me fit, but it's not as good as Denis's over there." He points to a man picking gooseberries and listening to the radio, which is just too loud for him to hear the compliment.

Then Val comes along and invites me to have tea and biscuits in her beautiful plot stuffed full of healthy veg, pretty flowers and scarecrows of the local newsreader and weatherman. She lets me sit in her favourite comfy chair and we talk of animals and gardening. Like me, she has too many animals but she sells some of the veg she grows to help pay for their upkeep. I take note.

People wave good morning as we sit in the sunshine chatting and Val tells me she's just graduated with an archaeology degree and now everything takes her twice as long because she's always looking at every little bit she digs up. Having also battled breast cancer, she says she is living every day of her life to its utmost. Her partner David comes and joins us after a while and tells me how the allotment has been a helpful distraction over the last few months as he has lost both parents recently: "You get perspective when you're here. You don't forget about them, but you know that they wouldn't want you to stop doing it. We've been coming here for 15 years. We love it."

Val tells me how everyone helps each other out and I can easily feel the friendly atmosphere for myself. "It's especially good for the old folk," she says, "because they're getting out of the house, seeing people and having a chat."

Each allotment has its own shed. Some are just sheds and some are welcoming little homes away from home – like beach huts but bigger – decorated with all sorts of paraphernalia, old and new. They make me smile and feel I could quite happily live down here. Val tells me that one early spring she came down and found a tramp had been living in her shed over the winter.

I meet Lance, the allotment rep, and his wife Marlene who are just as welcoming and smiley as everyone else. If this place isn't proof of gardening making you happy I don't know what is. I wish I had filmed my whole visit so that I could play it back to myself on dreary winter days.

Lance and Marlene escort me around the rest of the allotments – it is a huge area, much bigger than I first saw – and I meet more happy gardeners whose names I forgot to note. The top corner of the allotments seems to be reserved for handsome young men whose plots are no less impressive than the old boys'. One of them, Andrew, tells me he used to be a sportsman but suffered an injury and gardening has now replaced his sport. He tells me he brings his children down to work there too. "It's a community – everyone's got time for each other," he says.

Lance and Marlene point out the Bishop's allotment and tell me how the neighbouring plot belongs to an Irishman who swears like cor blimey which makes them all laugh. Another older chap, Peter, tells me how his allotment is the main reason he recovered well from a stroke eleven years ago. "I'm a lucky man – I walk here and walk back. It's like paradise." He jokes about being an illegal immigrant from Newcastle and that his teeth are falling out but all the while he is smiling and looking around at his roses and veg. "The grandchildren love coming down for the strawberries," he tells me, "they put their finds on facebook."

Two men come along, each walking with some difficulty and Lance tells me that they used to have the best plots on the allotment until illness meant they could no longer do the gardening themselves, but they still come down just to be there and keep in touch with everyone.

Lance has recently built an allotment shop which is also doubling as a meeting place for allotmenteers. People are already gathering there and I can see that it is going to be a jovial spot which may mean less work being done on the plots but more friendships made nonetheless.

Two young women approach Lance to find out about getting an allotment for the family and he welcomes them happily and assures them they will be able to have one quite soon. They're delighted. Lance tells me, "We have some family plots with mixtures of flowers and veg. Some have just half a plot to start with because a whole plot looks daunting – so they start off with a small bit but then as they progress and get more enthusiastic they often want to take on another bit."

Then a lady called Katie, and her dog Bluey, come to invite me to see their allotment. On the way we pass the community garden area, which any member of the public can come and use. There's a couple weeding who stop to pass the time of day and as we move on I get an irrational desire to have an allotment myself, which is silly because I have acres at home. So it must be something to do with wanting to be part of this friendly club. And having a shed. Quite a lot of shed envy today and Katie's is possibly the funkiest so far, with pretty wallpaper rescued from a shop that was closing down. This is just one of the clever money saving ideas that makes Katie's plot so fabulous. Ingenious recycling and upcycling all over "I get lots of stuff from skips – I see people taking things down and say 'Ooo do you want that?'"

She shows me her 'Eden Project' – mosquito nets from e-bay being used to protect her brassicas from the cabbage white butterfly. "I've been gardening a very long time," says Katie and shows me every single plant enthusiastically. "Look, red Brussels sprouts! I just love it – I practically live here. I grow everything from seed. This is Eau de Cologne mint." Katie darts from one joy to the next and I happily follow her around her plot. "I noticed my first tomato yesterday!" But her peas are scorched and we puzzle why "especially when the sweet peas are doing so well". "That tree died – I rescued it from a Poundstretcher shop – gave it a good

Daisy on the Lotties

Water feature in Ramsbottom

Miranda & Jill's Garden

A nod to the local weatherman

Me with Lavinia

Katie's Beverley plot

Val on her Beverley allotment

home, watered and tried to save it, but now it's being used as a support."

We stop briefly to eat the wild strawberries and Katie and I agree they are even nicer than the big ones.

Katie tells me she works as a carer so sometimes doesn't come down until evening and only goes home because it's dark. It seems to me that the garden cares for her after her day of caring for others.

With little spare money Katie finds a cheap way of doing everything – her scarecrows are dressed in charity shop finds and simply made with plant pots linked together. An old wine rack is being turned into a bug hotel. There are so many ideas and so much being said that I can't write it all down quick enough and still see everything she wants to show me – it's not easy this journalistic thing.

There's been something so exciting about visiting the allotments – so many different gardens so close together, creating a huge tapestry of natural beauty and human endeavour. It is glorious. Local artist Jo Pearson can often be seen painting here, and I can totally understand why; with flowers like corncockle; cornflowers and teasles growing wildly next to a neat row of leeks and onions; next to a brightly coloured shed; scarecrows; bunting; CDs swinging in the breeze; the Minster in the background, the bright colours of marigolds and nasturtium; and the searching tendrils of runner beans stretching happily up their canes. It is as pretty as a picture.

But time to go back over the bridge, which has a special place in the hearts of my hosts too, "We've lived with it since it was first built – in fact we used to go every fortnight to watch it being built," says Marlene. "We love walking across it."

Returning to the bus, I make a quick phone call to the person who has left a note on my windscreen asking if they can hire the

Daisybus for a wedding. I am so tempted to agree, but have to say I'm not local and hope they find someone else nearby. And then, with the unmistakable roar of an old VW engine I'm off. Today has been a good day and I feel on top of the world in more ways than one.

Jill & Miranda's Garden

This time I'm off to the north of Lincolnshire and it comes as a surprise that it reminds me a little of the Cotswolds – but paying attention to the map for a moment tells me that I am in the Lincolnshire Wolds so that explains that. It's pretty and I find myself in a quiet village called Goulceby to meet Jill Mowbray and Miranda Manning Press whose lives are anything but quiet. As well as being gardeners, they are garden designers and florists who grow their own flowers for wedding commissions and they run workshops on floristry. They also help with several community and school gardening projects and practice Thai Yoga Massage from a wooden chalet in the garden.

It was the mention of therapy in the garden as well as gardens as therapy that made me want to meet these ladies. "We are great believers in the therapy of gardening and the holistic benefit of the beauty of flowers and plants," Jill tells me and, despite my evangelical proclamations hereto that gardens are soooo good for you, it is time to admit that sometimes gardening is flipping hard work. Jill and Miranda know this very well.

With years of working in healthcare, as well as a keen interest in sport, nutrition and, from what they tell me, overdoing it trying to help too many people with their gardens, these ladies have learnt a thing or two about wellbeing.

"We need to respect our bodies and look after them" they say and I guiltily admit that I haven't been so good at taking care of my own body. I come out of a lazy winter and go hell for leather, working through the early spring, accepting the aches and pains and trusting that my body will get used to it soon – which it has done 'til now. But I am getting older and listening to Jill and Miranda, I know I really have to start being kinder to myself. "Without our health, life can be pretty miserable," they say. "But if you listen to your body when it whispers you won't hear it scream." This is good advice my body whispers to me and I wonder whether I dare mention my bad neck – I don't want them to feel they have to help me while I'm here.

But my neck isn't under a lot of strain right now as we sit in the garden eating delicious home-made cake and drinking coffee. I can manage a tour of the lovely garden too. Because they're florists the garden is full of flowers – lots of annuals like Cosmos, Love-in-the-Mist, Marigolds and Zinnias but lots of perennials and useful foliage too. As members of the organisation Flowers From the Farm, they fervently believe in the motto 'Grown not Flown', something which, when I was a florist thirty years ago, (OMG), was pretty much unheard of. Most blooms were flown in from Kenya or Holland. Crazy really, when Britain is a nation of gardens.

Spending so much time helping the community, and generally being friendly gregarious sorts, it's not surprising that Miranda and Jill like to have some privacy in their garden. As they show me around I feel it is a cherished place and that their relationship with their plants is particularly intimate – perhaps because the plants are their work tools, or maybe workmates. I can imagine the ladies monitoring the plants' health and posture as much as those of their massage clients.

With their garden opening on Sunday, the kitchen is full of cakes and the living room is full of local friends and artists' stuff too enticing to ignore. I am allowed a sneak preview and bag myself a few lovely things – it's all for charity after all.

My stiff neck has been noticed and before I leave I have it stretched and kneaded the Chiang Mai way until it feels good enough to hunch back over the steering wheel of the Daisybus and wend my way home.

It's the end of July and to be honest I'm starting to feel tired from all this driving. I love the Daisybus but she's not a smooth ride and ergonomically she's disastrous. I'm also suffering with some sort of bug and, as I set off on the long journey towards my next clutch of garden visits in Norfolk, Suffolk and Bedfordshire, feel a little sorry for myself. At least I have the luxury of Stephanie Challinor's new purpose-built Shepherd's Hut to stay in. I fall asleep on the comfy bed almost as soon as I arrive.

I wake to find myself in a lovely garden surrounding a very attractive house. My hut (if something so lovely can simply be called a hut) is surrounded by wild flowers and perched above the lake – or is it a moat? The Challinors are new to gardening and after a lifetime of travelling the world are loving their new life which combines being at home creating a fabulous garden with running their Bed & Breakfast.

Breakfast is served in the main house at Bays Farm where I am told I can also have supper when I return from visiting my next garden. So, nicely nurtured and feeling much better, I set off from Norfolk to meet Jean and John Walton an hour away in Suffolk.

Jean's Garden

As I enter the garden room of the Walton's house my first thought is "Wow – a typical NGS garden!" I'm not sure exactly what I mean by this, except that it is incredibly well planned, well planted and well-tended garden full of colour. Island beds and wide winding grass paths lead this way and that, with something new and gorgeous at every turn. This is a high maintenance garden and it doesn't surprise me to learn that Jean spends most days out here.

She tells me, "I think I got my passion from my grandfather who taught me to garden when I was a toddler. He worked at the end of the road and would come home at lunchtime. We used to eat our lunch as quickly as possible so we could garden before he had to go back to work."

"I would have loved to be a gardener but in my day only men took it up as a career," Jean says. But since retirement she and John have realised her ambition of designing and creating a garden "of a reasonable size". Their 1.4 acres at Dunbheagan is the result. It's been hard work. First they had to clear the site of 100 pine trees.

The second job was to surround the garden with rabbit fencing. The third was to increase the height of the rabbit fencing when they discovered how high they were prepared to jump! Then the muntjac deer arrived, too.

It's a big sunny garden with A LOT of plants in it. This could have been expensive if Jean didn't love taking cuttings and sowing from seed. She shows me greenhouses packed to the brim with young plants. They don't appear to have a problem with slugs, probably because of the huge toad population. They once found 43 in a greenhouse and sometimes there are so many out there you can hear them crunching on the gravel at night.

I settle down for my own dose of calming gardening, after which I am treated to a lovely lunch and some funny stories from John. He is a Geordie with a mind full of curious facts – not least the origin of the word Geordie. Apparently back in the day, two miners' lamp hats were invented: one by Humphry Davy – used by the Yorkshire and Lancashire miners – and another one created by George Stevenson used by the Tyne & Wear miners. Thus the Tyne and Wear miners became known as Georgies – now Geordies. I'm learning so much more than how to grow a carrot on this trip.

I notice the art in the house and find out that the whole family are artists. Their rooms are decorated with pastels by daughter Debbie and wildlife illustrations by their son Andrew alongside Jean and John's own pottery and paintings. Andrew's talent won him the RSPB Artist of the Year Award. Surrounded by such talent, Jean is modest about her own painting but tells me it is much like gardening – when you're in the zone it is totally absorbing.

We do a little more gardening after lunch and time flies. I'm lost in this jungle of choice plants and by the time I leave (after being treated to tea and cake as well) I realise the bug that was bugging me has thankfully buggered off – told you gardening is good for you.

Back at Bays Farm I take the opportunity of exploring this garden of symmetry, shape and contemporary planting, so different from where I spent most of the day. This is the beauty of gardening – there are many types of beauty. This is the beauty of life.

Kate's Garden

'Elf' and Safety is a phrase usually followed by a chorus of 'gawn mad' when someone in the pub tells us that conkers have been banned in schools or social workers aren't able to help up someone who has fallen in their home. I confess, I have always had a somewhat indifferent attitude to H&S myself. Until, that is, I travel to Bedfordshire to meet Kate Gardner whose job, as a Facilities Manager, is to make people's workplaces better. Better for safety yes, but what I learn from Kate is that these days there is a really positive movement towards making work environments better for the health and wellbeing of workers as well as making them environmentally sustainable.

Kate's work deals with exteriors as well as interiors. She knows that green, natural surroundings have a beneficial effect on workers. At her own workplace, Kate has recently made a garden people walk through to get into the building. She has planted roses, lavender and sage. These help make people feel good when they arrive for work.

Inside there are a number of initiatives for a healthy workforce; persuading people to walk to work; stand up meetings; using stairs rather than lifts; healthier options in cafeterias; getting rid of unhealthy vending machines. There are lunchtime walking clubs, groups of gym goers and cycle to work schemes. Kate also implements changes in the way offices are laid out; maximising light, using colour and putting up photographs of outdoor scenes. I wish Kate had been around when I worked in an office. Had I suggested back in 80s that it would be nice to have a picture of a bluebell wood and a few plants around I would have been labelled 'a bit of a hippy'.

As well as making life better for people at work, Kate shares her love of gardening at home, which is why she and husband Andrew open their garden for the NGS.

From their kitchen window I can see a large sheet of water over a stainless steel background. It's a really impressive first sight but also shows me straight away that this was once a really awkward plot – rising steeply from behind the house. Terracing is the obvious answer but not so easily achieved. This was a not a garden for the faint-hearted. However, Kate and Andrew cleverly designed it so the initial rise of land is used to produce this stunning waterfall. It has high walls either side and a really beautiful walkway and bridge along the top and at the bottom of the water there is a deck area. Steps rise up either side of the deck to the wooden walkway made by Andrew (handily, a cabinet maker by trade).

The design has a contemporary feel with a Diarmuid-Gavin-inspired surprise on the next level. In fact, arriving at the next level is a surprise in itself. Then on the garden goes to a further terrace. It's all planted by Kate who particularly loves the slow, nurturing process of gardening. "I like to watch something and see what happens – I'm not into instant gardening. I like the process of splitting one plant and waiting for its separated parts to bulk up – in the meantime I use annuals to fill the spaces."

"After work I'll come out with a cup of tea in one hand and secateurs in the other." She shares the advice of an old gardener: "Don't think 'I need to do that.' Do it! Deadhead or weed every day or there'll be twice as much tomorrow!"

But Kate enjoys it too: "I'll sit here with a glass of wine just looking and listening to insects and birds." She and I do just that for the rest of that afternoon.

A Perennial Garden

I was lucky enough to escape the suffocation of office life and swap it for half the pay but twice the happiness in the great outdoors. But sometimes professional gardeners fall on to hard times. The charity Perennial was set up to help. A little known charity, it's actually been going for 175 years (first known as the Gardeners' Royal Benevolent Society). It helps gardeners in crisis, whether with housing, disability, illness, bereavement or the challenges that come with old age. Jobs in horticulture are not highly paid and a number of horticulturists find themselves facing debt and financial hardship. Perennial helps them get on top of things and build a more stable future.

Perennial has been gifted three gardens; in Yorkshire, Herefordshire and Suffolk. Today I am heading to the one in Suffolk – Fullers Mill (previously owned by plantsman Bernard Tickner, who is still in residence). The relationship between benefactor and beneficiary is two-way: Mr Tickner gets the reassurance that the garden he has created over 50 years is looked after in perpetuity and Perennial get a fabulous garden they can open to the public to raise money.

I meet Annie, Head Gardener, and her team, who initially seem shy which makes me feel shy too. It soon becomes apparent that I am not a professional journalist, just another gardener and Annie takes me on a tour of the garden. As we walk she tells me, "I trained in horticulture straight from school and when the kids were young I worked for myself. I did a degree in horticulture when they grew up."

She suddenly screams and darts away from me, then runs over the bridge we were about to cross. I look around confused and from the other side Annie gasps, "Reptile!" "Lavender!" and I see two lovely grass snakes have draped themselves over the lavender to soak up the late morning sunshine. It's a delightfully unusual sight for me but Annie has a real fear of snakes, which after all is one of the rational fears of humans, and I'm not sure if it's thoughtful to mention that, when I was gardening in Australia, there was a constant threat of what might emerge from the bushes there. But it's too late – the words have escaped from my mouth.

I try to make up for it by saying it's a good thing the garden attracts wildlife and Annie points to a lake over the fence: "It's a conservation area – we have corridors to allow the wildlife in and out. Otters come in at night." Right on cue a kingfisher flits past us.

Annie shows me around the whole garden which fills me with admiration. The professional training shows – in the same way the lack of it shows in our garden – but it still manages to look like a 'natural' garden. "It's a very peaceful place," Annie says, "We can have 50 or 100 people visiting and it's still quiet."

We head back to join the others for their tea. (I stand bravely in front of the lavender to shield Annie from the snakes.) As I sip tea and eat biscuits outside the information office, Charles the Old English Game Bantam comes to see if there are any crumbs going. Annie says he is small but feisty and likes cake, which has caused problems with visitors in the past.

I'm envious of these three gardeners who have always known they wanted to work as gardeners. I think of all the time I wasted in offices. George the apprentice tells me, "I started animal studies but that didn't really go anywhere so I swapped to this. My uncle's a gardener so I've always been around it and I've always wanted to work outdoors."

Heather retrained when her youngest child started school. "I wrote to lots of different nurseries and got a job as a gardener/handy person for a sheltered accommodation block and also did some private gardens. I tried to get the old people involved at the home but it was hard because we only had a very limited budget. Because of this I used to grow stuff from seed and sell it to get more money to buy other plants."

I ask the gardeners if things have changed under Perennial's ownership but they say that the charity don't interfere with the day-to-day running of the garden; they are more involved with helping people who need it. "They have Outreach Workers – care advisors dotted about the country. So if someone contacts them and says, 'my husband's broken his leg and I've got six children to raise and we've worked in horticulture all our lives' – they put them in touch with the right organisations to make sure they get the help they're entitled to" Annie tells me.

As we drain our tea mugs, they ask if I'd like to help in the garden so I go and spend a pleasant hour planting, chatting, weeding and watching the tree surgeon's attempts to pull a tree out of the canal without making a mess of the surrounding area. Then, after a few photos with the Daisybus, I head off again into the Suffolk countryside.

I've been advised by my hosts at Bays Farm to stop in Bury St Edmunds if I get the chance, so that's where I point the bus. The town's sign says, 'Bury – Britain's Floral Town' and it's a lovely town – I spend most of the afternoon in the Abbey Gardens, snoozing and watching how the gardens are used by everyone. There are businessmen and women, with their jackets over their shoulders; mothers with small children picnicking; slightly older children running around the ruins showing off and arguing with each other; teenagers in groups under the trees flirting, laughing and screaming; students sitting quietly, chatting – perhaps planning their futures, just starting out on their adult lives. I watch them and think "I wish I was you" but then I qualify it: "with what I know now".

Paula's Garden

One final night in my snug hut before I head home, via Kettering in Northamptonshire. On the way I follow another campervan. Following a campervan is like watching yourself driving ahead and I remember how much I like campervans and it makes me smile and wish we were all linked with some sort of CB radio so we could say hello. As it is, we wave wildly at each other with big cheesey smiles that say, "Oooh look, you're like me – I'm like you!"

In Kettering, Ady Mantle brings me and his wife Paula some tea in a garden full of colour. Before I arrived they were in the process of painting a table pink. It's a small, town garden but it's gaily decorated with bright flowerpots planted with colourful plants. They discuss whether the campsis will be blooming for the NGS opening because the bright coral of its flowers will look so good next to the table and chairs.

Paula tells me, "This is our second year for the NGS. We're the only one in Kettering. We've had quite a few visitors. When they came they said there were advantages to it being in the town centre and liked the different ideas for a small town garden, as well as ideas that I've been able to do on a table top really. I can't bend down and work on the ground because this side of me is paralysed."

When Paula wrote inviting me to her garden she told me that, after a fall in 2010, she was partially paralysed, but her garden is her soulmate and her reason to get up in the morning. I knew I wanted to meet this lady and now that we are sat in her garden together I ask her to tell me her story.

"Well, I was on holiday in Ibiza five years ago – it was just a fluke accident really – I was walking down the street and just slipped – it was quite a shiny surface. I don't really remember anything – my foot just went and I instantly felt pain from the middle toe to the middle finger, which they told me later is the bit that serves your lungs, and that's why I wasn't breathing."

"So you were on your way out?" I say with great delicacy.

"Yes," says Paula, "Just from slipping on the pavement. We were two days off coming home and I ended up staying another sixteen weeks."

"There's no intensive care in Ibiza so I had to be flown to Majorca – I can't remember it. My heart stopped too – because if you stop breathing your heart stops. They had to resuscitate me and snapped a couple of ribs in the process. That was Saturday and I woke up on Tuesday not knowing where the hell I was. I was in a spearmint green room and people, well – they just weren't very nice. It's common – really common – for holiday makers to have accidents over there so it was run of the mill for them. If you fall in Ibiza they assume you're drunk because it's the party island. But it was four o'clock in the afternoon and I hadn't been drinking."

I'm not going to give you all the details of Paula's story because she is going to write it herself but, suffice to say that Paula, Ady and their then ten-year-old son Jamie spent a hellish four months in Majorca. Even when it was finally decided to risk flying her home, complications and relapses occurred. As I listen, I shake my head and gasp in disbelief. Paula says, "It just went on and on and on – relentless really. When we look back we realise we were just desperately paddling underneath, thinking 'we can't see the end, this is something beyond us'. There were many times I felt I wasn't going to make it through."

"I was losing myself – beforehand I was a confident, roof-off-cool-car kinda girl, with heels and designer jeans. I had everything I wanted – good job, nice family. I was stripped of everything. I was a wreck. When they first started to suggest taking me outside I wouldn't go – I was scared, scared of feeling fresh air on my face and of the traffic – I was petrified of everything."

"When I came home just going into the living room was awesome because obviously I'd been in a sterile room for a long time. It was magical – and it still is magical five years on. Ady got all the tables by the window and planted lots of pots with bulbs so I could see them inside. I wasn't interested in gardening then – it wasn't that I wanted to come out and do anything, it was just colour as opposed to black and white and clinical."

I'm a lucky shepherd

Theo and Albert in the 'Soldiers Garden'

Jean in her garden

Plant a Garden Grow Happiness

Kate and Andrew's great achievement

Jean's Wow Suffolk garden

Paula and Ady working in their garden

Michael, Richard and Penny at Lewis Cottage

"The following April a little old lady asked me 'Do you garden?' when we were waiting for the physio. I said 'not really' and she said 'I saw a such-and-such bird this morning – that's the first sign of spring'. She suggested I should go out into the garden. And then the more I thought about it, the more determined I became. But you forget how much things have changed. I stood by the washing machine, bent down to put my boots on and went flying. I couldn't stand on one leg to put them on like I used to! In the end I came out with both my hands in Ady's hands and we started off down the garden together." My eyes fill with tears.

"There was a massive Tasmanian fern that had completely died and everything else was just a black mush from the frost. I felt completely overwhelmed. I couldn't dig and I didn't know what anything was called. A friend of ours said she knew someone who might come and make a start. He came in the winter and he said 'Don't look at everything, just look at one area and start.' We began to watch Alan Titchmarsh and he said, 'Don't worry about what you can't grow, worry about what you can and do more of it.'" Good advice as usual from Alan.

"That's what we did, and it really took off. There was a rhododendron in the corner that hadn't done anything for years. I started to read and realised they like acidic soil and ericaceous compost. I cut it – followed the diagram on the internet and waited for a year to see if I'd done it right. Ady still wanted instant results but I kept saying to him 'it's a bit like being a patient – you've got to be a patient patient and you've got to be a patient gardener. Nothing is instant for me now. That's how is became the Recovery Garden. Two years later that we spoke to the NGS and the County Organiser said yes because of my story."

Life is more different for Paula than any of them could have imagined five years ago. We talk about her writing her book. "I suddenly feel an amazing sort of renewal. I feel like I can write my story now. I feel I'm on the edge. I can inspire others. That is the purpose of all this – does that make sense?" I nod, afraid to speak in case I cry.

Michael's Garden

There's something very exciting about visiting gardens south of your own. You expect to see all sorts of exotic things growing in the hot sun, people gardening barefoot and ending the day eating outside under the shade of an arbour. If I had gone further south than Cornwall this may have been true – maybe I need to do my next book on how gardens affect the lives of the French, Spanish or Greeks.... Would the Daisybus manage the distance though?!

It's late in the summer holidays and I've brought Willy, my nephew Theo and his friend Albert, down to Devon with me for a little holiday, combined of course, with some garden visits. We're staying in Boscastle so first of all I take the three of them to see Concrete Carole's garden and they are all duly wowed.

The next day, the boys and I leave Willy to have some time alone on an alien planet (he reads sci fi) and set off to visit a garden made by Michael French, who opened his garden for the NGS for the first time last year.

The boys' enthusiasm for the garden disappears the moment two puppies come skeltering towards us with Michael's wife Shirley. I abandon the four young things rolling joyfully around in the long wet grass of the meadow to visit the garden proper.

Michael tells me, "My motivation for making this garden was initially my son, Richard. He has served several tours to Afghanistan. During these tours he lost several friends. Other friends suffered life-changing injuries. I wanted to create a space where they could enjoy the peace and quiet of the English countryside they missed so much while they were away."

Set quietly around a picturesque thatched Devon cottage, I can easily imagine those boys dreaming of home – of this place – while facing hell in Afghanistan. "We're a military family. I've recently retired as a colonel. Shirley was an army nurse and officer. Our other son is also in the army. Although it sounds like a cliché, soldiers really do think of the green green grass of home when away – it drives us on. I remember some tough times in Bosnia when I often thought of the fields from which I was so far removed."

The garden here at South Worden is perhaps what any foreigner would imagine an English cottage garden to be. But it has some bold touches, like a massive stone with a hole through the middle which is a perfect photo opportunity for the boys.

Despite his own injuries, Richard has himself taken over another piece of garden to build a kind of posh campsite – a yurt and two very attractive sheds turned into kitchen and bathroom. Shirley tells me, "These boys don't give up easily – and they look after each other. If someone can't walk they carry him – and they'll probably all be laughing and messing about at the same time. Richard has just broken his shoulder in fourteen places and lost his right bicep in a parachuting accident, but it doesn't stop him," she says. I squirm at the thought.

Their son's endurance may be army trained and it's also perhaps a family trait, as his parents have both recently fought their way back to health from serious illnesses. The whole family is made of good, strong stuff and I guess they are exactly the sort of people the army needs.

To me the garden is a tribute to their allegiance to their country – and to life itself. This idyll might well be what a doctor would have ordered for this family and others in years past – 'a convalescence in the country' –away from the hurly burly of life in cities and the politics of the world.

The paradox of this gentle garden and its associations with war zones made me again so thankful for my good fortune to live in this country and to have the freedom to spend my time engaged with the beauty of nature. And yet, hearing of the bravery and the determination of the injured, and the friendships created during a soldiering career, I felt a little envious of a life that creates such strong bonds, reliability and trust in each other.

Judy's Garden

Another fine day and the boys are spending it with Willy, learning their seabirds from a boat, while I go off to Yonder Hill Garden near Sidmouth. Judy McKay has created a garden pretty much single-handedly over the last thirty or so years. Now, though, Sharon Attrell and her partner have joined her there to help. With Judy's partner and her daughter, Jenny, they all live together in happy self-sufficiency in a garden made with love and as much concern for the non-human inhabitants as the human.

Sharon says, "We first came here to install hidden cameras to capture the wildlife. We had a security firm but the recession hit hard. When we came here we just clicked with Judy. She needed help and wanted this place to continue after she'd gone, so it all seemed to fit perfectly."

Judy tells me how she started the garden "When I came here I ran a market garden and a wholesale nursery and had a few animals. I was making just enough to pay my electric bill and for the things I couldn't make myself – like soap and toothpaste. But the tax man didn't believe I wasn't making a fortune. The bailiffs came saying I owed 6k! They closed me down and I went on income support – they'd rather I claimed income support than be self-sufficient!"

"So I gave away the tunnels – I continued to feed us on £36 a week. I get Jen's allowances (she is disabled) which helps me a lot. We ate the animals and I made cheese."

"The garden started because I used to teach pottery and had a giant heap of ash sitting there for 18 months and we were wondering what to do with it. We decided to dig it in and plant something. Then we thought the mahonia we'd put in looked lonely and so it grew and grew, and grew!"

On their kitchen table is a strand of vine. "We're trying to find out if we can eat vine leaves like spinach, or in salad. Everyone uses them for wrapping things, but what else?" We all try a bit and look at each other. "Nothing wrong with that," I say. "I like that citrusy burst," says Sharon. "Hmm it's nutty. Wow – that's good!" says Judy.

Judy takes me through to the most amazing 'Drying Room'. It is packed full of dried food – gooseberries, raspberries, bananas – every fruit you can imagine. "We don't have freezers because of the cost – a freezer would have to stay on all the time. This drying machine only runs for 24 hours. Then we're just storing the stuff." I am reminded of Edward Acland in Cumbria and his preference for bottling rather than freezing. Judy tells me that health-wise it is much better to eat dried or preserved food.

"It's also a great way to deal with gluts. Like strawberries – if you haven't got time to make jam now – dehydrate now and then make jam in the winter when you've got time."

"The grocer brings me boxes of bananas because people won't buy them when they've gone spotty. And melons, trays of peaches, boxes of plums, pineapples – he can't sell it quick enough and it will just go off. I slap it all in the dryer."

The ladies announce it is time for a tour of the garden and we go to collect a scooter for Judy. Sharon explains, "Judy had a tumour on her spine – it's all sorted now but I told her to use the scooter anyway. It's really helpful in the garden because it's so big. Now I've got one too! They're great for carrying big bags or buckets for weeds."

The garden is indeed big – and full of interesting trees and shrubs that Judy has collected over the years. She's a woman who really understands her plants' needs and thinks hard about where to place them. The planting is thick and lush and you can hear but not see the chattering of wild birds and domestic hens . It is very apparent that, in this garden, wildlife is revered as much as plantlife. Bees, hoverflies, dragonflies, damselflies and butterflies are everywhere. I see my first Silver Washed Fritillary butterfly slowly flapping around us, in no hurry to move away. It's as though they know they are safe here. We pass through Dormouse Wood and then under an Owl Hide. Judy says, "The most important part of life at Yonder Hill is being in harmony with Mother Nature."

Sharon and Judy laugh when I ask if there is anything they would like me to do. "There's always stuff to do…! Particularly dead heading at the moment – fancy deadheading some buddleia?"

"Sure," I say, "sounds like an easy job on a nice sunny day."

"It's never-ending!" they say.

Visitors are welcome at Yonder Hill and there is now a self-service tea room for which Sharon makes cakes. "The garden gives people what they need – it might not always be what they thought they wanted but it provides the peace to accept what is needed. A recent visitor told me, 'I got a big green hug' from the garden."

Jenny has spent years caring for others; her Mum while she was ill, Jenny and all the domestic and wild animals at Yonder Hill. "This garden has really kept me going," she says and I can sense the embracing nature of this place – the mature trees and bushes, the simple buildings, holding this extended human and wild family together in mutual love and respect.

Michael's Garden

Forty miles away in Spreyton I am experiencing bumpy-track envy as I bounce along towards Lewis Cottage, owned by Michael and Penny Pell and Richard Orton. I'm a little nervous because I know from his emails that Richard is a Butler, but the address is definitely Lewis **Cottage.** I just hope they're not being ironic with the name and a huge country mansion is about to appear before me. However, the track goes on until I am fairly certain that no self-respecting Lord of the Manor would put up with these holes on a regular basis. I do duly arrive at the most idyllic cottage deep in the Devon countryside.

Richard invited me because Michael had been a finalist in the Gardening Against the Odds Awards. These awards were set up by The Conservation Foundation in memory of garden writer Elspeth Thompson. As I pull the Daisybus into the drive, a fit, smiling man strides across the garden to welcome me. "You must be Sarah," he says and I know I'm meeting Michael but am confused because, well, because there doesn't seem to be anything wrong with him. "Hello – are you Richard or Michael?" I say. "I'm Michael. Come in come in. Let's get a coffee" and I follow him down the steps into the pretty little cottage kitchen.

Later he laughs when I admit my first thought. Michael has made an incredible recovery from a stroke – a spinal stroke in fact – that could have left him paralysed for life. "I was gardening at the time and I thought a deer had kicked me in the back," he tells me. "I had to drag myself up the garden to find Penny."

The doctors told Michael that if he didn't walk within the first two months of having the stroke he would be unlikely to walk again. "I made sure I did," says Michael. Wife Penny says to me, "He's a very strong man. He wouldn't allow himself to be paralysed and confined to a wheelchair."

At first Michael asked Richard, who they share this place with, what jobs he could do sitting down on the ground. "I just shuffled around the borders, doing what I could and I gradually got myself up – this garden saved my life."

It is a lovely garden indeed, with a mix of traditional rose parterre, a stunning wet woodland full of primulas and skunk cabbage and contemporary ideas like a rill of camassia. Every area has a story. The bench made for his sister-in-law out of the tree she used to smoke under at school. The Smoking Border which used to be where Michael had bonfires. He was notoriously bad at lighting fires, he tells me, and was surprised one day when a visitor said, "Your bonfire is going well". He had been mowing and thrown a cigarette butt onto the pile of dead wood as he passed. For the first time, he had successfully lit a fire with ease. The only problem was the oak tree nearby had gone up with it, and the flames were threatening to destroy the field of corn next door. The fire brigade came and ended up staying the night to be sure the roots of the tree weren't still smouldering.

When Richard isn't a butler in London he is the propagator of plants at Lewis Cottage. Michael takes me to see the 'workshops': several polytunnels and greenhouses full of young plants. "Richard is the one who really knows his stuff. He's very knowledgeable." Indeed Richard's propagating has reached such levels that he now operates a mail order business – Lewis Cottage Plants, which he manages to do mainly at weekends when he returns from London. Penny too has an interest in the garden, although she works full-time. Her main interest is in growing veg and flowers to cut for the house. "I won't let her cut anything from the garden," admits Michael who, like me, wants flowers to be where he's planted them, not removed and displayed elsewhere. I shall have to start a cutting garden. The shoe is on the other foot though, when it comes to the wild flowers in the woodland – Penny protects them fiercely when Michael threatens them with the strimmer in late spring: "I'm not allowed to strim until they're finished".

The Bothy in the garden is currently a holiday cottage – and now a Flowerbed – and this must be one of the most tranquil settings you would ever find for a holiday.

Helen's Garden

Only a short while ago I wrote in my blog that I am not a plantswoman, but today, after ten minutes with Helen Brown I want to put that right. I want to join the club. I finally get it.

Helen describes herself as a plantaholic and I feel the affliction catching me as she walks me around her amazing garden at Little Ash, near Honiton. Her borders are like walking round a beautiful interiors shop – I want **everything.** As in those elegant, irresistible shops things look so desirable because of the way they are displayed. Helen has arranged her plants so well that each one is showing off its neighbour as much as itself.

Wide grass rides run down the middle of the garden, leading off into the Devon countryside. They remind of me of many a grander property, but, where the borders in those grand gardens sometimes leave me a bit bored, Helen's borders are exciting – every step brings another joy, an explosion of colour, a 'Ta Da' display, grasses raining like firework fountains behind the glamourous front-of-border plants.

Helen is out here every day – and it shows. "It's pure enjoyment," she says. "I come out and say hello to the new plants – I love to really look at the detail of a flower and I adore the things that smell."

Helen's mother taught her the names of wildflowers when she was little and from then it's been natural to be a gardener. She trained in agriculture and is married to a farmer so she has always been close to the land. Her farming links are evident in the garden, with well-placed, rusty farming tools and machinery adding to the spectacle. I'm particularly envious of the great granite rollers on show on the lawn and I become totally obsessed with a rusty windmill sculpture forming kaleidoscopic shapes in the breeze. This garden has to be one of the favourites of my journey – have I said that a lot?

I leave feeling excited about the plants I am yet to meet and looking forward to getting to know my old favourites more intimately, too. I remember garden writer Mirabel Osler recommends using a magnifying glass for a totally new perspective on your garden and decide to take the time to do exactly that when I get home.

But arriving home to the chaos of summer rampaging wildly, I realise some tidying up is necessary instead – and lots of string. Why do I never put supports in place **before** things fall over? It takes a whole day to dead head all the roses. The house is full of sweet peas, with more climbing up and over the exterior of the greenhouse. The donkeys have gone feral, and looking gorgeous as they naughtily find their way through electric fencing. They've eaten the signs that say, "Please do not feed the donkeys".

So I have a busy week chasing my tail in my own garden before heading off for East Sussex for four more garden visits in the Daisybus – my penultimate trip. First stop: Copyhold Hollow, where I stay with Frances Druce who runs a B&B here.

Yonder Hill Garden in Devon

Helen in her Devon garden

Stylish rust at Little Ash

Little Ash Garden Devon

Owl hide at Yonder Hill

Frances's Garden

Frances used to do B&B initially so she could stay in this house, bought as a renovation project with the intention to sell on. After just a few days she knew it had to be her home for life. "This hollow induced a feeling of tranquillity the first time I came to view the house and that feeling has never left."

I am lucky to share in this for a couple of nights. Frances shows me to a lovely, old fashioned single bedroom and I feel like a child staying with my grandparents again. My window looks out over the lower part of the garden and I see I am once more in the company of a 'proper gardener'. It seems you go through phases of gardening. Phase 1: all gardens look bewildering. Phase 2: anything you try in your own garden is exciting and encouraging. Phase 3: you start to feel confidence in your gardening skills and the way your garden looks. Phase 4: you realise you are a ham-fisted amateur.

I can only hope that after this epic journey of mine, I will find there is a Phase 5 in which one's garden becomes as good as any you've ever seen, though I suspect Phase 5 is more likely to involve relaxing and just enjoying it anyway.

Frances has made this garden alone, although she now has the help of a WRAGS trainee a couple of days a week. Amazingly, she also renovated the house with the help of one other lady – her cleaner. It was a mammoth task, but ten years on, it is exactly as she wanted and it looks to me almost as it would have done when the house was built 400 years ago. The history is tangible.

Harry's Garden

The next morning I leave Copyhold Hollow to welcome its Thursday Visitors (Frances generously opens nearly every Thursday for the NGS during the summer) and I make my way to another ancient house – King John's Lodge near Etchingham. I've been invited by Harry Cunningham who has turned some chicken sheds and a barn in his mother's garden into a really rather stylish nursery, café and shop. This place has plenty to offer visitors whether they're gardeners or not.

There is a strong sense of place here – it oozes history. I assume initially that the garden has origins as old as the dwelling, but in fact Harry's father just cleverly designed the garden to complement the ancient house, even making a haha to add to the illusion of age. It is easy to see how Harry, who is a local history enthusiast, was drawn back here after a spell in the rat race. Though his parents were gardeners, Harry didn't really garden until he started growing veg on a windowsill in London. Various pots outside the door followed, and soon he was giving vegetables away to school kids passing on their way home. Then Harry returned to the family home in Sussex to convert the old agricultural buildings into, what is today, a really cool place to buy plants.

"I'm proof that it is possible to turn your back on the rat race," Harry tells me. "Even if you think gardening isn't for you, just having a walk around, looking at what's growing and breathing in the scent is enough to inspire even the most reluctant of us to put something in a pot and enjoy its beauty." And there are certainly some fabulous plants available here to start people off. I am particularly drawn to the ferns, which turn out to be one of

Harry's favourites: all sorts of lush, beautiful architectural greens. I wish I could fill the Daisybus with them and plant them in one of the shady parts of the garden at home, but frankly my funds are running low by now, so I have to choose just one. I instantly forget its proper name and it becomes King John's Fern.

Harry says he has a holistic approach to gardening and propagates a lot of the plants he sells from the gardens, so anything people see and like in the garden is very likely to be available to buy. It makes sense to grow more of what is growing well and it's always such a good thing for local gardeners to see what might work well for them at home.

Harry and his wife, also called Harry, are running this place in such an inspiring way. The café is gorgeous, with sofas and a wood-burning stove. There is a barn for functions. They have vintage fairs, and even a Fairy Hunt. The whole place welcomes you and entices you further into the wonderful world of plants and gardens.

Jean and Roger's Garden

Another cosy night at Copyhold Hollow and the next day I'm off to visit Roger and Jean Pemberton near Orpington. They've written to me with a similar story to Ruth's, back in Worcestershire – the story of a garden rather than the current gardeners. Like Ruth, Roger and Jean made an old lady very happy when she discovered that the garden she started is still being cherished.

Roger says, "We moved here 20 years ago, buying from vendors who were quite elderly and had really just tended the plants. They told us of Mrs Willis, who they had bought it from. She had developed the garden from little more than a building site to a spectacular display of ponds, specimen shrubs, trees and pedigree roses so good that it had won the 'Best Garden in Southern England' competition run by the local paper – twice."

"The vendors gave us a series of newspaper cuttings and photographs of Mrs Willis and her immaculate garden. From then on Mrs Willis became our icon. We were determined to get the garden to meet her exacting standards once again. Each time we made a change, we asked each other, 'Would Mrs Willis like this?'"

"We often wondered what happened to her, but knew she must be quite elderly. Then, last year, we were decorating and Jean got fed up with my mess and decided to go shopping. She immediately returned, very excited, and said 'You'll never guess who I've got here – it's Mrs Willis!'. As Jean had left the house a middle-aged man asked her if she lived there and then said that his elderly grandmother who used to live there was in his car outside. He was gobsmacked when Jean blurted out her name."

"Mrs Willis, now aged 104, came in and trotted down the garden almost in tears. She had assumed the garden would, after all these years, be a motorway or a block of flats and was thrilled to see that it was still a garden – and one that met with her approval!"

I am listening to the story as we walk around the garden, to which they have recently added quirky bits and pieces and special areas for their grandchildren to enjoy. The children make up their own games and have their own names for parts of the garden where they live in an imaginary world away from the grown-ups.

Roger tells me a story about how the grandchildren use the garden. "Our twin granddaughters were about six years old and their older sister about eight. We were having a big BBQ with lots of family and friends, including one particular friend who is big and very powerful but also gentle and sensitive. He saw a drowned rat in the pond and, thinking it may upset the little girls, he quietly fished it out of the pond with a garden spade, hoping to bury it out

Lewis Cottage woodland

Copyhold Hollow B&B

Copyhold Hollow Sussex

Roger & Jean in their Kent garden

More fun at Orchard End

King John's Lodge

A giraffe – why not?

of sight. Suddenly: a whoop of delight and a six-year-old screaming with excitement, 'Oh great, a funeral'. Our friend was quite confused but did as he was told. He formed the front end of the funeral procession, with the dead rat still on the end of his shovel, whilst the girls organised us into a respectful line of mourners behind him. I rather stupidly asked where we were going and was told, 'we are going to the garden cemetery of course'. I said I didn't think we had a cemetery and was told in no uncertain terms that there had been a graveyard in the garden for years –'follow us". By this time there was a procession of about twenty, all trying to keep straight faces. We were led down what I thought was a small path made by foxes or badgers leading to a spot about two feet square. We were all 'hushed' whilst our friend, David, reverently dug a little hole. I was told to make a little wooden cross which one of the girls placed at the top of the grave and we all stood in silence for what the girls thought was about a minute – about fifteen seconds really. We were then given a list: two frogs, a newt, one goldfish, a mouse and lots of snails: All similarly buried."

It's obviously important to Roger and Jean to please others with this garden but they're getting a lot out of it themselves too "It's so peaceful and mentally relaxing," says Jean. "You're always planning, always learning, improvising – and the more you get into it the more you realise you will never know everything."

"I'm never bored. There's always something to do – even in the winter I enjoy the planning – and of course there's the health aspect. Mrs Willis is still sparkling about the garden at 105 – surely proof that it's good for you!"

In one of two ponds there are lots of frogs – one year Roger tells me, they had so many that their NGS Open Day was sent into chaos when it rained and hundreds of them came out onto the lawn. "The grass seemed to be alive and no-one could walk round the garden," laughs Roger.

Geoff's Garden

It has often been a relief to me while writing this book that I never intended to write a proper gardening book, with proper descriptions of gardens, plants and designs. I admire garden writers all the more now I know how tricky it is. Thankfully I'm writing about the effect gardens have on people's lives and I have never been more grateful to fall back on that excuse than when I walk into Geoff Stonebanks' garden, Driftwood in Seaford. I will just say I have never seen a garden so packed full of plants and colour and joy.

So much has already been written about this garden, there is little need for me to say more. Geoff has won scores of competitions, been presented with lots of awards, appeared in gardening magazines here and abroad, had regular slots on the radio and become an old-hand at television appearances. Year after year, Geoff has won wide acclaim for his garden and it is all richly deserved.

But why? Well, he loves it, of course – he was lucky enough to retire young and pretty much devote his life to it. But Geoff isn't just doing this for his own pleasure – he has become an incredibly successful fundraiser. Over the past 6 years he has raised over £60,000 for charity. As well as opening the garden for the NGS, Geoff has come up with ideas for garden trails around his locality. The Mayor's Open Garden Trail and The Macmillan Coastal Garden Trail attract thousands of visitors and plenty of publicity every year and Artwave brings local artists flocking to display their work in the unique setting of Driftwood Garden.

I am visiting the day before this year's Artwave so the garden is, I imagine, looking as amazing as it is ever likely to, with works of art nestling amongst or flamboyantly rising above the flowers. The zenith is partner Mark's own studio full of his paintings and photographs. Walking up through a garden by the sea on this hot day, surrounded by beauty made by both nature and artists, I feel these bright images will be burned into my memory for a long time. We sit in 'Dad's Place' for a cool drink looking back over the artists' palette of a plot.

Chatting in the summerhouse, Geoff seems to me to be simultaneously modest and proud about what he has achieved. For this man – who must surely now be a darling of the charity world – has committed a large part of his life to raising money, not only through his gardening prowess but also his brilliance at attracting publicity. Being a gregarious character not afraid of the camera lens, he is able to use the attention focussed on him and his garden to achieve wonderful things for others – and I guess that is a good excuse, if one is needed, to keep on doing what he loves best – gardening.

As my visits to gardens for this year come to an end I have a weekend at home to enjoy the finale to our own garden's annual show. My niece Jessica has brought her dance troupe The Land Girls to perform a piece she has especially choreographed for our garden here at Brook Farm.

Having a houseful of young people always makes me happy and having these lovely young girls fresh from college embarking on their lives as adults, I was grateful again for what Jessica brings to my life. Watching them rehearse – working and playing together – and with the land, the trees and the brook here – I am touched by their intimate and heartfelt interaction with the place.

We are blessed with a fine sunny September day. 'Take A Walk

With Me' takes the audience through our gardens and woodland to the top meadow with performances along the way. It was like a thousand momentary sculptures – beautiful and moving and I very much felt that I wanted to share it with each and every garden owner I have had the honour of meeting on my journey.

Jonathan's Garden

One last fling this year – all the way up to the glorious Lake District. Willy comes with me and we are treated with extraordinary generosity to a room in a hotel owned by the man I've come to see. Jonathan Denby is a successful businessman-turned-gardening-enthusiast – who doesn't actually do any gardening.

Sitting above Grange-over-Sands looking out over the perilous Morecambe Bay, there is a garden carved out of the rock that formed the hill eons ago. This ancient land and the new sub-tropical garden he's created here started a whole new life for Jonathan. Yewbarrow House had an overgrown garden of about four acres when he arrived with his wife and three daughters in 1999. Jonathan started designing plans for this very difficult plot with designer and writer Christopher Holliday who, handily, lives nearby. Having succeeded in making this extraordinary garden he was asked to write an article about the history of the garden for the Cumbria Gardens Trust.

Jonathan tells me that this sparked an interest in garden history which ran so deep that in 2013 he completed an MA in Garden History. He is currently undertaking a PhD in the subject at Oxford University, where he is working on his thesis: 'Gardeners' Lives'. "Gardening has taken over my life," he says to me.

Needless to say, Jonathan and I were keen to meet each other as we are essentially both writing about the same thing – how gardens have affected people's lives. Jonathan's gardeners are long dead though. I'm ashamed to admit that I've only heard of one of his Top Seven Gardeners – people who have influenced garden design and aspirations and whose lives changed dramatically because of their imagination, creativity and hard work.

In a pleasingly circular way, his research is now reflecting back in to his garden and I get a preview of the busts he has commissioned of his Top Seven. They are currently sitting on the floor of his hallway waiting to be placed on top of his very grand orangery. The Orangery is just one of a number of impressive glass houses and follies Jonathan has had built in the garden – all reflecting his knowledge of the Edwardian and Victorian extravagances that few can afford these days. In any other place I might feel they were ostentatious but here they are right because they belong to Jonathan and reflect his own fascination with the gardens and gardeners of the past. I'm really looking forward to reading Jonathan's research, not least because we share a dislike of 'Capability' Lancelot Brown – which is practically heresy in the gardening world.

Jonathan now shares his knowledge with clients as a garden designer, a new career he runs alongside his hotel business, having made show gardens for Chelsea and Hampton Court Flower Show and taken part in the Gardening World Cup – yes, there is one!

But it's not all theory and pretty designs on paper for Jonathan – although he prefers other people to actually do the digging and sweating, working closely with landscaper Carl Taylor. He has a real interest plants and introduces me to many varieties I've not seen before. This spot on the west coast of Cumbria is sheltered and has a climate similar to that in Cornwall so a lot will grow here that wouldn't stand a chance back home in Worcestershire. Visiting as we are, in October, the trial beds of dahlias are still looking spectacular, as indeed is the whole place. This is one of those places that has to be seen to be believed and again, thankfully, you can on any number of open days for the NGS.

So, impressive buildings, exotic plants, amazing views, can this garden offer any more? Well, yes, Jonathan has a great respect for craftsmanship and likes to employ local artists. The renowned sculptor Alan Ward has undertaken a lot of stone sculpting work in the garden and Robert Moorhouse has been responsible for the metalwork. There are also cobblestone mosaics by Maggy Howarth.

Alan has had some fun in this garden over the past few years carving the limestone blocks that form a part of the landscape: a giant foot; a lizard; a snail; even a mini Petra; and my favourite, Colossus appearing to hold up the ground in front of the house. Jonathan likens the apparent struggle of the giant to a gardener's toil. Like the great landscapers of the past, Jonathan's strength comes from standing back and appraising, thinking things through and giving things meaning.

And so again, creativity is born from the land.... I find this everywhere I go – always something new, inspiring and uplifting. Always something that makes me wish I'd thought of it myself!

Peter's Garden

Peter Stott could teach me a thing or two – he's another extreme gardener who started Larch Cottage Nurseries when he couldn't find the plants he wanted for his garden. His home in Melkinthorpe is now home to the most extraordinary nursery I've

TV celebrities
Geoff & Christine

Jonathan
Denby

Camera crew
in Driftwood
Garden

Jonathan's heroes

Tread Gently

Art from the rock
above Morecambe Bay

Larch
Cottage
Nurseries

La Casa Verde

Me and Willy
happy buying
plants!

ever seen. Not only has it got the most impressive and extensive range of plants, an interesting garden and a vintage craft shop, it also has a stunning Italian-style restaurant – and I don't just mean the food. Peter re-built the derelict farm buildings and he didn't stop there.

Outside, the nursery itself is divided by pillars, walls and arches all built by Peter. It truly is the most amazing backdrop for plant buying with statuary and funky bits and bobs spicing up the rows of beautifully kept plants, trees and water features. In the summer you can sit on the vine-covered balcony of the restaurant looking down over it all and eat wonderful home-cooked healthy food. It is truly heavenly and clearly a popular place for locals and tourists alike.

Joy, who used to be a fashion journalist and now works at the nursery, shows us around and tells me, "Peter is always working on something." She loves coming to work partly because there is always somewhere beautiful to sit and take a breather during the day. She especially loves sitting and watching the dragonflies by the lake. Peter even topped all his achievements so far by proposing to his long term girlfriend Jo and deciding to build a chapel in the garden for them to get married in. It was touch and go on the timings but he did it and a beautiful day was had by all. Joy shows me the chapel which has an incredible artwork fresco as an added surprise on the inside walls.

Peter is clearly multi-talented – an artist, a builder, a nurseryman and, I think most importantly of all, a free spirit.

My own free-spiritedness is on the wane now and, after so long on the road, I'm looking forward to spending some time at home, reflecting on all I've seen, heard and learned.

Our gardens

Perhaps one of the most romantic garden stories comes from my own husband's family. When Willy's grandmother Dorothy Clive became ill with Parkinsons, her doctor advised that she should walk a mile a day. So Harry her husband decided to make a mile of paths around the old quarry for her (well to be more accurate he got his man Moore to make a mile of paths) and, once they were made they started planting rhododendrons and azaleas so that she had something nice to look at on her walk.

Now very much extended with stunning gardens and open to the public throughout the seasons, The Dorothy Clive Garden attracts thousands of visitors every year and is so much more than the original quarry garden around which Dorothy took her exercise.

The group 'Friends of The Dorothy Clive Garden' contacted us to see if our garden at Brook Farm might be suitable for one of their coach trips and of course we were delighted to agree to one of their number coming on a recce to see if the place was – well – good enough I suppose. So a very straightforward county lady came one day and chatted to Willy about his memories of his grandparents and the various characters who had been responsible for keeping it all going. Then she went for a good look around the garden.

When she came back to the house we slightly nervously asked if she thought it was good enough for the Friends to visit and she said

"W-e-ll – it's not really about the garden so much as the connection is it?"

We have often laughed about this genteel insult, but for me, she was ultimately right only not it in the way she meant it. Because, yes, for me it is all completely about the connection: The connection between me and The Earth.

As the writing of this book, and my Daisybus project, comes to an end so also does our time at Brook Farm. It is time to make a new garden and, boy, am I blessed to have inspiration from visiting some of the best gardens in the country over the past year.

Our new garden will be a series of gardens celebrating biophilia (my new favourite word!) and will be in no small part inspired by the people and gardens I have met on this trip. It will be known as The Daisybus Gardens and will be laid out in a way that creates an art work on the land, (although you will probably only appreciate that from an aeroplane!) I like to think of it as a decorative piece of jewellery I am laying on Mother Earth – a thank you to Gaia.

Land Artist Richard Shilling is currently inspiring me. He tells me, "Throughout my life I have needed significant time alone, it comes in waves and every three or four days I desperately need to recharge. I go out for a bike ride or simply a walk, visit the woods to make something or just spend a few minutes in the garden."

"It doesn't take long to quieten the mind, to pause the internal dialogue and open the senses when surrounded by nature. You may think that, in order to transcend, one must stand on top of a mountain or witness a grand wildlife spectacle, that only being struck full force between the eyes by nature's majesty will it lift you out of your body to a new place of wonder and beauty."

"Through my art I try to peel back the layers of nature and discover what is hidden beneath. I do this by working closely with certain materials Mother Nature gifts me. It gives me the opportunity to glimpse the edge of infinity, to see that her abundance and myriad of forms is all around us, within us and ever changing, growing, evolving and returning to the earth before beginning the cycle of life once again."

"Ultimately, art is an expression of an artist communing with what is inside them and the medium that they choose to work with. The artwork is only the visible end result of a journey that opened me up to my unconscious and my sum total of experiences, and the many moments I have spent in nature. To say that a sculpture depicts transience in nature, or the turning of the season seems trite, only a sound bite summary that shows the ice above the surface."

I would like to share with you Richard's final piece of advice to me: "Go and make something yourself, commune with nature and see what it is you see, feel what it is you feel. There's no special secret to it. Every breath we take connects us to all of nature, intrinsically linked and interconnected.

Lauren
Acres

A bit of fun in
Bwlch y Geufford Garden

Fantasy Peacock
by Team Acres

Woman and child
by Gay Acres

Flying fish

Epilogue

In Bwlch y Geufford Gardens back in Wales, Gay leans on a tree for support as she tells me about elf-like Lauren and I remember the times I have leant on trees and sobbed in the same way. It is a shared moment of deep pain until we move quietly on to another eccentricity in the garden and laugh at their love of Morrison's shandy that has enabled Jim to build a hut with walls built from the glass bottles. A Cheshire Cat grins from a tree, flying fish made from spoons dangle from the branches overhead and all sorts of carved sculptures and other curiosities appear along the paths. There is so much to make you smile here.

In Lauren's garden, where her ashes have been returned to the earth that created her, a fantastical peacock is the centrepiece. Designed by Lauren's sister, engineered by her stepfather Jim and made by 'Team Acres' Grace, Jim and Gay, it stands tall; proud of Lauren's life, not crumbling the way the family must have felt they were at times. Much discussion went into the production of this artwork and there was seemingly an impasse regarding the eyes – should they be coloured? What colour? Should the copper body be polished or left to weather? "Then," Gay tells me, "Out of the blue a vicar, who lives 15 miles away and doesn't really know us or the garden and couldn't have known about the sculpture, rang me and said she'd had a dream that we were making a sculpture and it must have green eyes left to weather naturally! We believe it was a message from Lauren."

My visit to this extraordinary garden in Wales was how I ended a journey full of amazing people who were willing to share their stories with me – a journey full of laughs, healing and inspiration, both personal and horticultural.

My heartfelt thanks go to everyone who contributed to this book.

Cuttings

"It's not so much a garden, more a world lovingly developed by us over 42 years."
Judy Cowan, Little Myles, Essex

"The garden was rather like sleeping beauty."
Vicky Farren, The Grange, Oxfordshire

"Perhaps fulfils Francis Bacon's maxim that men turn to gardening as it is 'The greater perfection'".
Ross Underwood, Hodnet Hall, Shropshire

"Something about the garden draws you out of yourself, and into the stillness and the beauty of it all. Yes, there are flowers and shrubs but somehow the garden, like many other NGS gardens is so much more than this. It's a place to be, a chance to soak up some of the peace that a garden creates; an opportunity to forget the busyness of life. I would call it a quiet haven, with the birdsong providing a constant reminder of our place in the natural world."
Jill Hilton, Courtlands, Lincolnshire

"There is simply something very enriching to work with the land and see our project as a heritage asset as much as just a garden."
Mike & Louise Madgwick, Edwardstowe, Dorset

"We are reinventing and enhancing what was ultimately the essence of what attracted us here in the first place ...... a sense of space and wonderment." *Jackie Maunsell, The Old Watermill, Cornwall*

"I have been gardening for many years and have always found it very therapeutic and rewarding. I think my garden is one of the things that has kept me sane! I am an obsessive gardener and find it is the best thing to keep mind and body occupied and thoughts away from things I can't change."
Lois Machin, Hardwycke, Sussex

"It's an interesting garden with an emphasis on humour. I think a lot of gardeners take themselves too seriously so that gardening becomes a chore rather than a pleasure."
Gilly Tugman, Winchelsea, Sussex

"When the hospital Chaplain asked where I went to church I said my garden was my church where I could contemplate and reflect on life in peace. Gardens do sustain us in times of crisis and need."
Katie Bunn, Whitstone Farm, Devon

"We enjoy being in nature because it is something in life that is being true to itself"
Cathy Anstey, Worcestershire

"My studies as a psychotherapist took me to research 'eco therapy' using gardening and engaging with the outdoors as a tool for repair and recovery. Whilst doing this I became ill myself with a nasty does of breast cancer which put paid to my career for a few years whilst I recovered from all that the medics could throw at me. My garden became the therapy for me to get well again and regain confidence in life. I spend as much time as I can growing, nurturing and creating our beautiful garden."
Nicola Talbot, Falconhurst, Kent

"I eat it, think it, drink it – I have a creative family and I think creativity is in your genes but comes out in different ways. My role in life is to be a gardener. I feel sure of that."
Phillipa Burrough, Ulting Wick Garden, Sussex

"Our garden is my oasis of calm and also my frustration. I dream of perfection, of heaven on earth, I plant, design, dig and the weather and the wind are my masters. I have to compromise and keep going, thinking of next year and how wonderful it will be."
Cecile Irving Swift, Bosworth House, Northamptonshire

"Opening for the NGS is a chance to help those in need at a difficult time of their lives."
Louise Martin, Fawley House, Yorkshire

"Thirty years ago I did not know a plant from a weed, but I soon learned that the garden was a place where I could escape. For me, when the textbook says "no" I will try and do it in any case. Having our business attached to the house it is important to create areas where we can feel we are somewhere else rather than at home."
Lieke Swann, Whyncrest, North Yorkshire

"I have a great belief in the positive contribution of gardening to mental as well as physical well-being"
Julia Faulconbridge, Whatton, Nottinghamshire

"Gardens without some humour can easily be soulless."
Chris Mortimer, Mill Barn, Lancashire

"Julie, our County Organiser, describes me as a garden decorator rather than a proper gardener – A description I am more than happy with because I don't have a great interest in the ins and outs of plants. I consider them ornaments with which to decorate my garden. It should also be said I have no interest in growing from seed, no interest in growing from cuttings and am a failed compost maker."
Peter Barrett, www.peteslittlepatch.co.uk

"The house and garden are surrounded by fields and therefore the design has reflected the need to make the garden and fields flow together whilst creating an environment for wildlife to also enjoy. Fruit and vegetables are used to provide food and drink for the table – I love preparing dishes using seasonal produce and my husband is very keen on making preserves. The enclosed patio area looks out on to the surrounding fields and it is a joy to be able to sit and enjoy a meal and glass of wine whilst listening to the birds singing (especially the sky larks). It truly is an escape from the rat race and the best possible way to recharge batteries so as to take on the challenges that life throws up."
Christine Sanderson, The Hollies, Derbyshire

"I have a love of plants; the more I look into their history, the more I'm fascinated. Colour, shapes, their likes and dislikes – they're like children."
Jane-Anne Morrison, Allsorts, Oxfordshire

"I have fallen in love with my garden and hope that I have begun a journey with it that will lead to the realisation of my many plans."
Lesley Manners, Bichfield Tower, Northumberland

Having bought a house with only a lawn surrounded by mature trees and an overgrown impenetrable woodland, I was compelled to make a garden. It brings me such joy, I really wish I had discovered it earlier: All those years of sheer bliss I've missed!
Maureen Kesteven, Ryton, Tyne & Wear

"Gardening is full of surprises. You think you've planted the vista in your mind and you get something completely different"
William Wint, Husband

"I have always believed in the power of the mind in particular as you get older. An active mind keeps the body healthy. The growing of plants is a challenge and is fascinating. I started gardening at the age of 14 when my father was taken ill and subsequently died. I have memories of a tulip tree on our lawn under which I sat with my Dad watching cricket. I planted one of those trees here which reminds me of my super Dad who I never knew as an adult."
David Sydenham, Durcombe Water, Devon

"Our garden is an outlet for artistic expression colour and fun."
Miranda Allhusen, Sutton Mead, Devon

"I have lived a Jobs Mill all my life. My mother and father poured a lot of love and time into the garden. I am trying to keep it going in memory of them."
Silvy McQuiston, Jobs Mill, Wiltshire

"The garden was my project to open and share my creation with like minded people. It has helped me focus and stay positive that there might be more life; it is so therapeutic. I lose myself in the garden and focus on the weeding pruning or potting. Art or clay has the same effect, it's about creating bird baths, sculptures and the feel of the earth between your fingers."
Julie Skinner, Cherry Hill, Derbyshire

My Mum was an avid gardener and her garden was a mass of colour throughout the summer and autumn. She died several years ago and I kept her memory alive by gardening. I have split the plants she gave me from her garden over and over to fill the space and keep the budget down and the husband happy. I love tending to the garden as it's like an adult version of playing out!
Anita Collins, Tetbury, Gloucestershire

"Our garden is so peaceful and healing that we wanted to share it with others. The NGS is for us, the perfect way of sharing and we also host garden parties for the local Stroke Club."
Cathy Toole, Middlewood House, Cornwall

"Opening for the NGS focusses the mind! We had 252 visitors, including the local school children and teachers who use the garden for school lessons plus 69 visitors by appointment, plus our open day when 67 visitors decided to brave the rain!"
Paul and Joy Gough, Sweet Briar Cottage, Wiltshire

I even dream about my garden"
Marion Jones, Tobyfest

"I used to inspect chickens innards – I prefer gardening. My best advice is to plant green side up!"
Rose Gregory, Tobyfest

"It's not a posh formal garden, but it would win The Most Loved Garden prize!
Pamela Thompson, Pear Tree Cottage, Worcestershire

"Gardeners are such amazingly nice people and gardening is calming and nurturing "
Jane McBean, Tobyfest

"My mother gardened 'til she was 97 – she was out there at 6am. Her garden kept her alive. She lived to 101 years old.
Maggie Hoskinson, Tobyfest

"Gardening gives you belief in yourself. And it's fun to watch the stoned bees in the echiniops"
Rupert Wade, Tobyfest

"We have been fortunate in a way as the garden here dates back to the start of mining in the late 1700s and my late father-in-law remembered it as a lovely garden between the wars, but this was destroyed in a Dig For Victory push by the tenant here during the war years. All this has meant having blank canvass and no fear of destroying something historic."
Charlie Pridham, Roseland House, Cornwall

"My husband and I moved here in 1987 – he was a very keen gardener, I mostly looked after the kids and did a few pots by the back door. He unfortunately died and I picked up the trowel and carried on. For me it was a big achievement to be accepted by the NGS; my garden is not perfect but I love it."
Helen Roberts, The Old Rectory, Cambridgeshire

"You can see your garden is put together by feel."
A friend trying not to be rude about our garden in Worcestershire

"This will be our 8th year of opening but this year has a special poignancy. I was diagnosed with breast cancer in August 2014 and am now benefiting from the help Macmillan gives. Hopefully I will never need Marie Curie as treatment is going well but I have done 18 weeks of chemo, had an operation and am about to start radiotherapy – and it all brings it home so powerfully when you actually need their help."
Christine Mackness in Devon who sadly died in February 2016

"We began the build of our Huf House not long after my stepdaughter died and I had had emergency surgery to remove a tumour in my spine. After such a difficult time, my husband and I put all our energies and creativity into planning the house and garden. At times it was quite daunting but gradually it came together and I have loved physically being in the garden, either weeding or moving plants or trying to grow things from seeds. I am learning as I go along with help from books and the internet. I have also grown to appreciate insects funnily enough. Things I would have screamed at before, I now see how beautifully they are made and I feel very brave."
Lynn Paynter, Whitehanger, Surrey

"I moved to Burrow Farm 55 years ago with my husband John to run a dairy farm. There was no garden at all but I started one in an old roman clay pit which was the only area not suitable for farming. Today there are 13 acres of garden and we are open every day from the 1st April to the 31st October. I have passed on my interest to my children with my son owning a landscaping business and one of my daughters being a garden designer and my grandson has worked for me in the gardens for the last 5 years and does all our social media as well."
Mary Benger, Burrow Farm Gardens, Devon

"I decided I wanted to open my garden after a very close friend died after a long battle with breast cancer. My garden is my sanctuary, it feeds my head and heart and something I think should be shared – it's the Wordsworth thing with those daffodils!! I get enormous pleasure from knowing people enjoy coming here – plus the charity contribution!"
Sue Emms, Ross-on-Wye, Herefordshire

"My dad was a superb gardener and instilled in me a lifelong love of gardening. Paul, my husband, has always wanted to open a garden under the NGS scheme so, when we were accepted, it was such a thrill. Also, the fact that so much money is raised for cancer care charities is very dear to my heart......my dad died of cancer when I was just 18 and I am a survivor of cancer myself."
"I think, if one is a keen gardener, and has a beautiful garden to sit in, when you are feeling under the weather or recuperating from a severe illness, it must help. I know it gave me something to focus on during the dark days of chemotherapy."
Pip Wadsworth, Ridgehill, Devon

I used to be a lawyer by trade and during my time in London it was not so much the gardening (four window-boxes!) as the plants that brought me a sense of peace. Weeding by the river I am often bathed in a feeling of gratitude for the place, the space, the privilege of being here as a custodian of this amazing place. For Steven and I, it's such a fundamental part of our lives, an essential way that we connect with earth and nature. Life without my garden is literally unimaginable."
Nicola Evans, Lower Grenofen, Devon

"We garden because we are passionate about it. We encourage wildlife and garden organically. I can't kill a thing – I wouldn't harm the mice who eat so many of my seeds, the moles who dig around the paths, the rabbits and hares who nibble the tender stems, the pigeons who demolish my brassicas, the butterflies who lay eggs on precious plants, or the blackbirds who devour many of my raspberries and strawberries just before they are ripe enough for us to eat! I believe the garden is for sharing!"
Vanessa Brown, Abbot's Barn, Cambridgeshire

"The gardens I've had through my life have been the core of my existence – nothing else offers quite the same stability and infinite chances of creativity."
Annie Bullen, Wildhern Gardens, Hampshire

"Fourteen years ago I got chronic fatigue. I think it was creating the garden that helped me get better."
Joy Martin, Wild Rose Cottage, Cambridgeshire

"I have a love of gardening which includes gardening as a therapy for all ages. I feel my garden gives ideas and inspiration for children and adults. I'm also involved with a charity that provides a wonderful opportunity for children to interact with nature."
Ann Moss, Harbourside, Hampshire

"As I walked the dogs each day through our Village of Weston-under-Wetherley, I admired many gardens and, in 2012, persuaded 10 fellow gardeners to agree to open their gardens alongside my own, for the NGS. We opened in 2013 with over 1,000 visitors, and then again in 2015 – this time with nine gardens raising over £4000 for the NGS. Besides the wonderful enjoyment of the weekend, we as villagers have enjoyed stronger relationships with gardening as our common interest. Personally, I have found great comfort in my garden when times have been difficult in my personal life, as you can tell from my poem a variation of David Ignatow's poem, 'Above Everything.'"
Bren Boardman, Weston-under-Wetherley, Warwickshire

'Above Everything'

I wished for a happier life often
but now that I am a gardener,
I have changed my mind about the World.
It should go on as it is, it is beautiful,
even as a dream, filled with
an abundance of hours tending
my glorious shrubs and perennials,
and planning my new allotment
a beautiful therapy,
if ever I have found one.
In the next world, should I remember
this one, I will praise gardening
above everything.

Bren Boardman, Warwickshire

Acknowledgements

My heartfelt thanks go to my father for his illustrations of the adventures of Daisybus – I wish I had inherited his artistic talent. Also to my sister for her proof-reading and loving encouragement. And to my clever editor Emma, at Orphan's Press, as well as Donna Wood for her support too.

Also thanks to Amanda Loviza-Vickery for her photograph (back cover) and cheerleading from the other side of the pond. The image of me having a lie down at the end comes courtesy of Ruth Edwards and my thanks to all others who contributed photographs including Alan Holland from TWIGS and Fiona Edmond from Green Island Gardens.

I would also like to thank the 400 people who invited me to their gardens – you were all an inspiration and encouragement and my thanks too for the support from the NGS Head Office team, County Organisers and other county team members who cheered me on and helped. To those who welcomed me into their homes and gardens: I am so happy to have met you and I thank you too.

Biggest thanks of all of course go to my husband Willy who was left looking after two donkeys, two sheep, one dog, two hens, twelve cats and numerous holiday cottage guests while I was gadding around gardens and eating cake.

And finally, thank you to you for reading. I'd love to hear from you so do contact me through my website daisybusgardens.com or follow me on Twitter @daisy_bus.